Natural
Calm

Other titles in the
Women's Edge Health Enhancement Guide
series:

Women's Edge
HEALTH ENHANCEMENT GUIDE™

Natural Calm

Stress Relief for Today's Woman

By Elizabeth Shimer, Mariska Van Aalst, and the Editors of

RODALE

© 2001 by Rodale Inc.

Illustrations by Shawn Banner, Judy Newhouse, Tom Ward

Cover photographs by Nancy R. Cohen/PhotoDisc (candle background), Hilmar (woman holding glasses and two women walking), Mitch Mandel (portrait of a woman), and Duncan Smith/PhotoDisc (woman receiving a neck/shoulder massage)

Printed in the United States of America
Rodale Inc. makes every effort to use acid-free (∞), recycled paper (♻).

Library of Congress Cataloging-in-Publication Data

Shimer, Elizabeth.
    Natural calm : stress relief for today's woman / by Elizabeth Shimer,
Mariska van Aalst, and the editors of Prevention Health Books for Women.
       p.   cm. — (Women's edge health enhancement guide)
    Includes index.
    ISBN 1–57954–420–7   hardcover
    1. Stress management for women.   I. Aalst, Mariska van.   II. Prevention
Health Books for Women.   III. Title.   IV. Series.
    RA785 .S535   2001
    155.9'042'082—dc21
                                                 2001002148

Distributed to the book trade by St. Martin's Press

2 4 6 8 10 9 7 5 3 1   hardcover

RODALE

WE **INSPIRE** AND **ENABLE** PEOPLE TO IMPROVE
THEIR LIVES AND THE WORLD AROUND THEM

FOR MORE OF OUR PRODUCTS
WWW.RODALESTORE.COM
(800) 848-4735

Natural Calm Staff

EDITOR: Debra L. Gordon

WRITERS: Elizabeth Shimer, Mariska Van Aalst

CONTRIBUTUNG WRITERS: Marcia Cronin, Bridget Doherty, Patricia Dooley, Kimberly Flynn, Diane Kozak, Jennifer Kushnier, Linda Mooney, Bebe Raupe, Alison Rice, Carol Sorgen, Dayna Winters, R.D.

SERIES DESIGNER: Lynn N. Gano

COVER DESIGNER: Leanne Coppola

PHOTO EDITOR: Robin Hepler

ASSISTANT RESEARCH MANAGERS: Sandra Salera Lloyd, Shea Zukowski

PRIMARY RESEARCH EDITOR: Anita C. Small

MANAGING RESEARCH EDITOR: Carol J. Gilmore

LEAD RESEARCHER: Elizabeth B. Price

EDITORIAL RESEARCHERS: Lori Davis, Debora Dellapena, Adrien S. Drozdowski, Jennifer Goldsmith, Lynn S. Goldstein, Lois Guarino Hazel, Jennifer P. Kowalak, Josh Popichak, Dorothy A. West

COPY EDITORS: Amy Morgan, Anne Winthrop

EDITORIAL PRODUCTION MANAGER: Marilyn Hauptly

LAYOUT DESIGNER: Bethany Bodder

PRODUCT SPECIALIST: Brenda Miller

Rodale Women's Health Books

VICE PRESIDENT, EDITORIAL DIRECTOR: Elizabeth Crow

EDITOR-IN-CHIEF: Tammerly Booth

PRODUCT MARKETING DIRECTOR: Guy Maake

WRITING DIRECTOR: Jack Croft

RESEARCH DIRECTOR: Ann Gossy Yermish

MANAGING EDITOR: Madeleine Adams

ART DIRECTOR: Darlene Schneck

OFFICE STAFF: Julie Kehs Minnix, Catherine E. Strouse

Contents

PART FOUR
Finding the Calm

Introduction

I write this in the quiet of my office, the scent of orange blossoms from the aromatherapy diffuser perfuming the air, soft jazz on the radio. All is tranquil, peaceful . . . and unusual.

For, like most of you, I rarely find such pockets of calm in my go-go life. And even when the opportunities for relaxation and serenity *do* present themselves, it's rare that I can convince myself to take advantage of them.

But after working on this book, I'll be better able to recognize—and benefit more from—those pockets of serenity when they arise, even creating some for myself. And that's our hope for you, too.

This book is the ultimate antistress guide for the ultimate stressed-out being: the 21st-century woman. Today stress is as much a part of our lives as e-mail and pizza delivery. It hits us from every angle—work, home, marriage, kids, just *getting* to work.

How stressed are we? Evidence suggests that nearly every visit women make to the doctor is stress-related in some way, and stress-related conditions are responsible for more than half of the 555 million workdays lost each year.

When the writers and I sat down and thought about the stress in our lives today, we were reminded of Dante's Hell, a series of nine levels, each worse than the next. Part Three is modeled after those nine levels—with solutions and strategies that work. The all-female writing staff of this book ferreted out both the tried-and-true and the new-and-improved methods for stress relief today, ranging from learning how to breathe properly to using needlepoint to dissipate your tension. Sure, we tell you about using exercise to relieve stress, but we come up with some unique ways to do it—including yoga, tai chi, and kickboxing. We've developed an antistress diet—perfect for that week before your parents come to visit, the month of December, and the day you have the big presentation at work.

Speaking of work, this book devotes an entire chapter to dealing with stress in the workplace. We teach you how to assert yourself, with both your boss and your coworkers, how to say no, and how to recognize the signs of impending burnout before the flames start licking at your motivation.

The result is advice from dozens of experts—including medical doctors, psychologists, therapists, and time-management gurus. But we've also gone to the greatest expert of all—you. Throughout this book, you'll find dozens of real women explaining how they overcame their own stressors to find a pace of life that left them not only happy but healthy as well. We hope this book will do the same for you.

Debra L. Gordon
Women's Edge Editor

PART ONE

Stress in All Its Glory

Stress: Defining the "S" Word

Pick two of the following words that best describe your life: *Chaos. Tension. Serenity. Fatigue. Contentment. Mayhem. Balance. Joy.*

If you're like most women, "balance" was not one of your choices. While we may dream of a life of balance, the way we live usually belies this goal. Instead of mixing equal parts of rest and activity, we're often trying to fit in one more dinner with friends, one more soccer fund-raiser, one more e-mail. Eventually, there's no wiggle room left within the demands we put upon ourselves, and we're stuck trying to find the true texture and meaning of our lives between dashes to the post office and 3-minute breakfasts.

Blame society and its pressure to do more, better, faster, *now*. If we're not doing something every possible second, we're afraid we'll be seen as weak-willed, unproductive, or lazy. It's a world in which we wear our stress and busy schedules like a badge of honor while inwardly mourning our lost calm.

The key to banishing this type of stress, say experts, is to stop looking outside ourselves for answers and start listening to our hearts telling us what we truly need. Once we do that, we develop an inherent sense of how much we can offer before we get to a breaking point. We strip away those things that don't add to our happiness and, so, slowly peel back the grip stress has over our lives. We spend less time with people who drain us and more time with those who enrich us. We have time to work on our dreams. We put our priorities first, understanding finally that supporting and nurturing ourselves is the best gift we can give our family and ourselves.

"If I had to define the opposite of stress, I'd say it's contentment," says Margaret Chesney, Ph.D., professor of medicine at University of California, San Francisco, and a principal investigator of women's stress for the National Institute of Mental Health. "That's not an absence of stress—it's a balance between the challenges of the world and your capacity to respond and grow."

The best news is that we already know what the solutions are—we just have to find the tools to uncover them. So think of this book as an enormous tool chest, one in which you can pick your own device from thousands available to help you tune out the noise and tune in to your purest purpose.

Stress, Defined

Say the word "stress" and it sounds like the hiss of a snake, coiled as tightly as our tense muscles. We know what it feels like as we ricochet around our lives, constantly changing directions and reacting to other people's needs, enduring breathless days of feeling five steps behind no matter how fast we run. We choke down aspirin to banish headaches, caffeine to stay awake, mood boosters to counteract crippling anxiety and depression.

Strictly defined, stress is a real or interpreted threat to our mind or body that makes us take action. With that description, stress encompasses all challenges, whether dangerous or exciting. Stress includes both the stressor (the thing that taxes us) and the stress response (how we react to that taxation). This response can affect us in four ways.

Physically. Stress causes a chain reaction in our bodies that begins with the release of the hormones adrenaline and cortisol; they quicken our pulse, increasing the flow of oxygen to our brains and shutting down our immune systems and digestive functions. This "fight or flight" response evolved so we could react appropriately in a threatening situation, recover quickly, and move on. Stress becomes dangerous when we experience this response too often or for too long.

Behaviorally. In a perfect world, we would respond to stress by getting more sleep, eating better, exercising, and soaking in a nice, hot tub. Unfortunately, we more commonly resort to coping mechanisms such as smoking, drinking, overeating, and abusing drugs.

Emotionally. Our emotional sensitivity is part of what makes us good communicators and intuitive nurturers. But this sensitivity can get overloaded in times of stress. When we're feeling overwhelmed, we may feel hopeless, anxious, and easily upset. As awful as these emotions are, the far end of the stress spectrum is almost unspeakable—crushing depression and, sometimes, even suicide.

Intellectually. Short-term stress can make us feel sharper, thanks to the increase of oxygen and blood in the brain. That's why students often get hooked on the habit of cramming for tests— they feel more focused and energized the closer they come to the test. But if you continue to use deadlines as a crutch, your stress addiction can backfire—long-term exposure to stress harms your memory and decision-making ability.

The secret to managing stress is to learn how to turn on your own response in amounts adequate to meet your daily challenges and then turn it off when it's no longer needed. Simple, huh? Well, this simple trick has become the focus of a multibillion-dollar stress-management industry; the subject of thousands of studies, books, workshops, and motivational seminars; and the source of obsession for countless researchers since the beginning of recorded history.

The Truth about Stress

One step in the recovery from stress addiction is learning the truth about stress. Here are some of the most common myths about stress. Holding on to these false beliefs may hold you back from your well-deserved calm.

Myth: Stress is the same for everyone.

Reality: Stress is different for every person every minute of everyone's life. Whereas one week you can take everything in stride, the next week the same stressor makes you feel like the world is collapsing around you. We never experience stress the same way as someone else because we had different parents, ate different food for lunch, are at different points in our menstrual cycles, or spoke to different people that day, says

Daniel Creson, M.D., Ph.D., clinical professor of psychiatry and behavioral sciences at the University of Texas Medical Center in Houston.

In fact, new research suggests that the old paradigms about how we experience stress may not even hold up for women. A landmark study, published in the journal *Psychological Review* in 2000, suggests that women experience stress very differently than men do. Men react strictly with the typical fight-or-flight response, and although women may react to stress the same way initially, our reaction can better be defined as a "tend or befriend" response.

Researchers from UCLA theorize that this tendency arose out of biological necessity—mothers with small children weren't able to run quickly, so they sought to protect themselves by building up social networks (befriend), and their first reaction to a threat is to shield their children (tend). For more on this phenomenon, see "Making New Connections" on page 118.

Myth: Stress is always bad for you.

Reality: Stress gets you out of bed in the morning, spurs you to look up in the dictionary words you don't know, prods you to take care of your children and think about your career. Stress challenges us and keeps life interesting, says Bill Crawford, Ph.D., psychologist in Bellaire, Texas, and author of *All Stressed Up & Nowhere to Go!: A Guide to Dealing With Stress and Creating a Purposeful Life.*

In fact, according to an Ohio State University study, *brief* bouts of emotional stress may temporarily improve immune function. In animal studies, researchers found that hormones released during stress sent protective cells called leukocytes from the bloodstream to the skin.

WOMAN TO WOMAN

She Jumps Out of Planes to De-Stress

During the week, Mandy Hampton, 35, is the editorial director of a hectic Los Angeles photo syndication agency. But come Saturday, you'll find her a few miles above the earth, diving headfirst, up to 180 miles an hour, toward the ground. Skydiving charges Mandy up, giving her the energy and happiness she needs to get through the next week—until she can jump again. This is her story.

Ten years ago, I jumped for the first time. I wasn't scared at all—I was excited and happy. I was attached to a jumpmaster as a tandem passenger, and because he was in charge, I relaxed and handed the responsibility to him. My heart was pounding, but it wasn't fear. I've always been excited by adrenaline sports, but I'm not a sporty person—it's always the adventure things that get me going.

As a student at the University of California, Berkeley, with little cash, I couldn't continue jumping. But about a year ago, I wanted to get my boyfriend a birthday gift he would never get for himself, so I signed us up for tandem jumps. It was very stressful for him. He didn't relax until he got down to the ground, but I couldn't wait to do it again. Since then, I've done 200 jumps.

While I'm in the air, I'm ecstatic. My brain goes into overload, and my thoughts are completely shut down—it's just sensation. I'll do a sunset jump, and the beauty just awes me. When you're falling through space at up to 180 miles an hour,

This reaction, researchers say, may be a way that short periods of acute stress ready the immune system for battle.

"If we experience stress once a week—like getting cut off in traffic—it pumps our blood quicker and cleans out our arteries," says Dr. Crawford. "Once in a while, it's a very natural, healthy response." It's when we experience it long-term—like when we rail nightly at our fellow commuters for their idiotic driving—that our immune systems weaken, he says.

with nothing but air around you, it's like you're flying. You don't have any weight; your spirit gets bigger than your physical body.

In the beginning, I would shake for an hour and a half afterward. I wrote notes in a logbook, but you can't read anything—it's all chicken scratches. Now adrenaline is like a drug—I get blasé about doing the same kinds of jumps, so I have to mix it up. I'll go head-down, 180 miles an hour, instead of floating on my stomach at 120 miles an hour. When I get something right, the adrenaline gets going again, and I'm happy for a good hour afterward.

When I first started, the happiness lasted all week long. Now the happiness lasts all day. If I don't jump for a couple of weeks, I get more stressed out, I don't feel as relaxed or confident, I get depressed. It's like I'm in withdrawal.

But skydiving has changed my life entirely. Anytime I start to think, "This is too much—I can't handle this," I think, "What am I saying? I jumped out of a plane!" Even my vocabulary changed—now when I'm faced with challenges, I'll say "Bring it on!"

I've cut away a lot of silliness in my life. Because I'm involved in the entertainment industry, my life used to be "follow the party." I've made a lot of great new friends through skydiving—from astrophysicists to mechanics—but I don't see my old, entertainment-biz friends that much. I still make an effort to see the ones who are worth it—but now my priority is jumping. I have more energy and a better appreciation for my life because I'm doing what I want to do.

the children. Many stress-management techniques begin with self-care, such as getting adequate sleep, proper nutrition, exercise, and enough time for personal fulfillment. Whether your self-care is meditation, a balanced meal, or even an invigorating walk around a museum, your instruments—your brain, your emotional capacity, your heart and lungs—will become more finely tuned and better able to handle whatever the world throws at you.

The benefits are twofold: first, most self-care involves healthy activities for body and mind, strengthening them to better cope with stress. Dr. Creson points out that 2000 world chess champion Vladimir Kramnik won against the unbeatable Garry Kasparov because he was more physically fit. Thus he was able to sustain higher levels of energy, better handle the stress of the competition, and focus for longer periods.

The second, and possibly most important, reason for self-care is that it gives us a sense of control, a touchstone of personal confidence. If you can find 20 minutes a day to do something *you* really want to do, that power transfers into other areas of your life. Deliberately making time for self-care gives you experience in setting boundaries and priorities, the number-one way to reduce stress, says Dr. Crawford.

Myth: Stress is everywhere, so you can't do anything about it.

Reality: Despite the constant pressure to produce at all costs, when you give in to this pressure, you're making a choice to deny your own true nature. "A lot of people's stress and worry comes from trying to fit into a life where they're asked to be something they're not," says Dr. Crawford.

The first step in learning to control stress is putting your own needs first—yes, even before

Myth: The most popular techniques for reducing stress are the best ones.

Reality: The most popular techniques for reducing stress—such as drinking, smoking, overeating, even endlessly talking about the problem—can actually make matters worse. Dr.

WOMEN ASK WHY

What is it that makes one person's hell another person's heaven?

There's the woman who loves jumping out of planes and the woman who can't even get on a plane. The one who tries a different restaurant every night and the one who pitches a fit if her favorite item is taken off the menu at the diner. People probably inherit a tendency to deal with stress within a certain spectrum—some families will be full of sky divers, some full of librarians. But what's at work here is not only the genotype (our genetic structure) but also the phenotype (genetic structure plus environmental influences).

For example, a thrill seeker in an Amish family will probably never become a big-time risk taker because the environment doesn't support, encourage, or stimulate it. On the other hand, the same person in the Evel Knievel family may be only too happy to carry on the family tradition.

Thrill seekers nurtured with positive influences and exposed to novel situations, complex projects, high intensity, and low structure may develop into entrepreneurs, creative scientists, and artists. They become people who change the world. But when thrill seekers are tempted by negative influences—like drugs, alcohol, or unsafe sex—they may become extremely destructive and delinquent.

It's important for parents to identify this thrill-seeking behavior early and offer constructive outlets. Kids also need experience in taking risks so they can better calculate the outcome of risky situations.

Our level of desire for thrills may change over our lives, but it won't go away. For example, after breaking nearly every bone in his body, Evel Knievel decided to stop jumping canyons, but now he's an artist and an entrepreneur.

Expert consulted
Frank Farley, Ph.D.
Professor
Temple University
Philadelphia

Chesney calls these "avoidance behaviors." They're not limited to obviously destructive habits. For instance, when stressed you may eat a lot of junk food, or stop eating altogether. You may spend much of your free time zoned out in front of TV or doing simpler but unimportant tasks.

"These activities affect your moods but don't affect the source of stress," says Dr. Chesney. "Using avoidance behaviors can make you feel better in the short run, but in the morning the problem is still there—and in many cases, even worse."

The best stress-reduction techniques help you ferret out the root of your stress and tackle it head-on. If you're upset about your job, instead of complaining with friends at happy hour, spend that time looking through the want ads, reading *What Color Is Your Parachute?*, or talking to a career counselor, says Dr. Chesney.

Even when there's no solution to your stress, you still have the power to choose a positive way of dealing with it. If you're stressed because your father just died, "ask yourself what you loved about your dad, and re-create those qualities in your own life," says Dr. Chesney. "If he was a thoughtful person, emulate his example by sending letters to friends." Positive stress reduction helps you use the problem to learn and grow—avoidance, a form of negative stress reduction—can make the problem even worse.

Myth: If you have no physical

symptoms of stress, you have no stress.

Reality: Physical symptoms are only one-quarter of the stress-response pie. Even if you don't get frequent headaches, upset stomachs, colds, or flu, you may be become anxious, depressed, or angry, eat or drink more, or temporarily lose track of some brain cells.

For stress has a serious effect on brain function. According to a study published in the *Archives of General Psychiatry*, high levels of cortisol, one of the hormones released under stress, can cause a temporary decrease in memory. Chronic overproduction of cortisol may also be a contributing factor in depression and dementia in our later years.

Sometimes this memory lapse may be more than just inconvenient or embarrassing. When we're stressed, we may "forget" to eat well or take our medication. "We sometimes lose the motivation to stay healthy when we're feeling stressed," says Dr. Chesney. "Right when we need to take more care of ourselves, we tend to take less."

Myth: Only major symptoms of stress require attention.

Reality: If we paid attention only to major symptoms of stress, more of us would end up in the emergency room, attached to heart monitors. We need to pay attention to small signs that might otherwise escape our radar, such as headaches or a sore jaw, indications that we may be clenching our teeth, says Dr. Chesney. You may find unexplained

WOMEN ASK WHY

What makes some people stress resilient?

Resilience is part of human nature. Some people have tremendous capacity to deal with high-stress situations without really breaking down. That doesn't mean these people don't feel stressed, agitated, and anxious; they just have a better ability to handle it. They may have inherited the genetic part of that response from their parents, but a great deal has to do with how they were raised and how they currently lead their lives.

People who have a firm sense of who they are, have accepted responsibility for their own lives, and have learned to deal with problems seem to deal well with stress. A big component in this is the ability to set priorities and identify your limitations.

A person who bounces back from stress is flexible—she handles her life well, but not compulsively, identifying the things that are impossible. Less flexible people have more problems with the negative consequences of stress.

While you're experiencing stress, tell yourself, "I can get through this"; it's a powerful message that will get stronger each time. Study your own early-warning signs so you'll know when you need to take better care of yourself, slow down, set priorities, and get social support.

In a sense, stress is valuable education. It provides opportunities to win, to lose, to struggle. Through these opportunities, and with good mentoring, you can learn to approach stress with more confidence.

Experts consulted
Daniel Creson, M.D., Ph.D.
Clinical professor of psychiatry and behavioral
*   sciences*
University of Texas Medical Center
Houston

Margaret Chesney, Ph.D.
Professor of medicine
University of California
San Francisco

bruises or notice that your skin is unusually dry. Even chapped lips and hangnails are signs of stress, because when you're under stress, you tend to lick your lips and pick your cuticles. The key is to identify your stress warning signs and use them as reminders to step back and care for yourself.

Women may also experience fluctuations in their cycles and even skip their periods entirely because of stress, says Dr. Chesney. They may also gain weight around the middle—cortisol has been associated with increased belly fat, a proven risk factor for heart attacks.

If you're tired all the time, you could be lying awake through part of the night, a victim of chronic insomnia. Based on studies, researchers theorize that stress-induced insomnia could increase your risk of a heart attack. Or stress may dampen your libido—when you're subconsciously worried about other things, you don't have the desire to seek pleasure in any form.

Myth: Stress is entirely environmentally related.

Reality: If this were true, we'd have no heroes. Think of the men and women who run into burning buildings to save sleeping children or volunteer for active duty during times of war. Everyone responds differently to stress—certain people even thrive during times of high stress, says Dr. Creson.

This difference is probably genetically related, but we can also complicate our own reactions to stress. When we hold negative images in our minds, we create chemical changes within our bodies equal to any outside force or illness, says Dr. Crawford.

To understand this idea, close your eyes and think of biting into a lemon. Your tongue probably puckered at the thought of it—you produced a chemical reaction to an image in your mind. "When we imagine a stressful situation, our bodies react as if we are actually experiencing it," says Dr. Crawford. If we switch to a more pleasurable image, such as how we'd *rather* be feeling, we can elicit the opposite response—the release of beta-endorphins, nature's painkillers. This habit of replacing negative thoughts with positive ones is called purposeful thinking. Some people call it optimism, or holding the belief that whatever happens, I can handle it. A recent Harvard study linked optimism with greater physical and mental health and vitality and lower levels of physical pain.

Myth: Stress is all in your head.

Reality: "Stress is all in your body" would be more appropriate. Our hormones play a tremendous role in the way we experience stress. Because of rapid shifts in mood-regulating estrogen, women are more likely to suffer from severe stress and anxiety during their premenstrual periods. Some women even suffer from premenstrual dysphoric disorder, or PDD, a debilitating condition that can feel like stress overload but is actually a severe reaction in the brain chemistry to the normal ebb and flow of reproductive hormones.

Sometimes stress comes from elements not only beyond our control but outside space and time. When the body's circadian rhythms are thrown off—as when you travel across time zones or work the night shift—you may produce more cortisol, which can produce harmful effects of stress even if your job is not stressful on its own.

Stress may not always be in your head, but the ability to learn from it always is. "Stress is a valuable signal, just like the lights in the dashboard of our cars," says Dr. Crawford. "The signals themselves are not the problem—they give us valuable information about something that needs to change." The problem is when we ignore them, instead of using them to turn our life in the right direction.

All Stress Is Not Created Equal

Stress is to the human condition what tension is to a violin string: too little, and the music is dull and raspy; too much, and the music is shrill, or the string snaps. The key is finding the right balance, learning how to manage the stress that comes our way. For how we manage stress determines whether it will be the spice of life or the kiss of death.

That's why stress management can be so complicated: we're not dealing with just one type of stress. There's acute stress, episodic acute stress, and chronic stress—each with its own characteristics and best treatments. Adding to the difficulty is the fact that we all react differently to stress. What sends one woman hiding under the covers may barely affect another. This book is all about managing stress. But you'll do much better with the tips and recommendations throughout if you first understand just what kind of stress you need to manage.

Acute Stress

The most common form of stress, acute stress comes from the demands and pressures of the recent past and the near future. While it can be exciting in small doses, as when you start a new job or buy a new house, too much acute stress is exhausting, says Washington, D.C., organizational stress consultant, psychotherapist, and licensed clinical social worker Mark Gorkin.

He likens acute stress to a fast run down a challenging ski slope. Exhilarating at first, that same run late in the day is taxing and wearing. And just as skiing beyond your limits can lead to falls and broken bones, acute stress overload can cause psychological and physical harm, says Gorkin, author of *Practice Safe Stress with the Stress Doc.*

During acute stress, adrenaline is released, triggering all the fight-or-flight symptoms. Acute stress also interferes with clear judgment and makes it difficult to take the time to come to good decisions. It consumes mental energy, leaving you distracted and anxious, and causes difficult situations to be seen as a threat, not a challenge. Irritability, anxiety, and depression are the emotional fallout from acute stress. The physical symptoms run from head to toe—tension headache, dizziness, jaw pain, backache,

Why is the incidence of anxiety disorder and stress-related illness so high these days?

More than 20 million Americans suffer from stress-related disorders, with job stress the most common source. While modern life is increasingly stress-filled, the real reason for the increasing numbers is better methods of diagnosis and the fact that these disorders carry less of a stigma than they did 30 years ago. Today, people are more aware of the role stress plays in their overall health, so there's a greater willingness to see a health care professional if symptoms become disruptive. In fact, the American Psychological Association estimates that 75 to 90 percent of all visits to doctors are for stress-related conditions.

And as the pace of our work lives has picked up, so has the number of people experiencing stress-related fatigue, exhaustion, and burnout. Balancing longer, more intense hours of work with the demands of family life puts a stress strain on most Americans, leading many to feel that there are never enough hours in the day. This sense of a "time famine" in their lives becomes an internally generated stress that can be resolved only by active treatment, such as employing stress-reduction techniques or time-management skills.

Expert consulted
Catherine Chambliss, Ph.D.
Chair of the psychology department
Ursinus College
Collegeville, Pennsylvania

These are the people who are always taking on one more obligation when they know they already have too much on their plate, or who keep trying to improve an obviously toxic relationship. They're the chronic procrastinators who rationalize that they do their "best work under pressure." They're the perfectionists who can't tolerate "a B+ every now and then," he says, or the malcontents who constantly find fault with the status quo and are always looking for a new job, a new apartment, a new boyfriend. Because the pace of our wired and Webbed world encourages frenetic action, with its accompanying stress, it's important to be aware of this unwitting addiction and take steps to avoid it, he says.

Realize that the feelings of stress are a signal—that you're doing too much, that the relationship isn't working, that you're expecting too much from yourself and the world—and then back off. "Don't be afraid to let people down a little bit," he says. Set boundaries, and when you find yourself feeling the need for a "stress rush," remind yourself that there's no need to overextend.

chest pain, shortness of breath, sore muscles, heartburn, flatulence, diarrhea, constipation, irritable bowel, and cold hands or feet.

Unfortunately, many people get hooked on the stress rush, says Gorkin. Without that "jazzed-up" feeling, life feels stultifying in its "screaming emptiness," he says, so "stress junkies" look for new crises that will provide excitement.

Managing Acute Stress

The art of acute stress management is to keep yourself at a level of stimulation that is healthy and enjoyable. One of the best remedies for acute stress: yoga breathing. It reduces acute stress response while allowing you a moment to "center" yourself, says Andrew Weil, M.D., director of the program in integrative medicine at the University of Arizona College of Medicine in Tucson and author of *Spontaneous Healing*.

Here's how it works: Sit with your back straight, and place your tongue against the ridge of tissue just behind your upper front teeth and keep it there. Exhale completely through your mouth, making a whoosh sound. Close your mouth and inhale quietly through your nose to a mental count of four. Hold your breath for a count of seven. Exhale completely through your mouth, making a whoosh sound, to a count of eight. "Do this breathing exercise at least twice a day," says Dr. Weil. "You can repeat the whole sequence as often as you wish, but don't do more than four breaths at a time for the first month of practice. This exercise is fairly intense," he says, "and has a profound effect on the nervous system—more is neither necessary nor better for you."

Episodic Stress

Women in the throes of episodic stress are always in a hurry, always late for appointments, always passing other cars on the road. They take on too much and can't organize the crush of self-inflicted demands clamoring for their attention. Their lives tend to be studies in chaos and crisis, their interpersonal relationships fraught with tension. Often, they're ceaseless fussbudgets, "worrywarts" who see disaster around every corner. Or they may be prone to aggressive, type A behavior—

MORNING MANIA

Is this scene familiar? With 5 minutes until the school bus comes, you son is still searching frantically for his math book and left shoe. You notice a grease spot on your silk blouse and rush upstairs for a replacement. Your husband can't find the car registration he needs to buy a new license plate today, and your daughter is waving a permission slip in your face that must be returned this morning or else she can't go on the fifth-grade field trip.

Morning mania is a fact of life for most American families. But there's a simple way to get out of the house in the morning with your blood pressure intact, says Mark Gorkin, a licensed clinical social worker and author of *Practice Safe Stress with the Stress Doc*. A reduced-stress morning begins the night before, says Gorkin.

If you have children, take half an hour or so in the evening to address school matters—sign papers, review homework, and so on. Be sure that your kids have their book bags packed, ready to go, and at the front door before bedtime. Have them choose and lay out their clothes, in one specific spot, to prevent morning fashion emergencies. You do the same.

Prepare lunches and store them in the refrigerator, to be grabbed before departure. Prime the coffeemaker so that all you need to do is start it. If you have one with an automatic start function, use it.

Plan tomorrow's breakfast and assemble all the ingredients, including putting out on the counter the bowls and spoons for cereal. Think about anything else you'll need tomorrow (the dry cleaning, the papers for the bank), and put them near the front door.

Building these rituals into your evening will give you the luxury of time the next morning, says Gorkin. Use that time to connect with your family before you all fly off in different directions. "Busy people don't make time for each other, which leads to an impoverished family life. Spend 5 minutes in the morning 'eyeballing' each other, making real human contact. It will reduce everyone's stress susceptibility for the rest of the day."

BLAME IT ON STRESS
Hair Loss

You've heard of the woman who suffered a great shock and suddenly her hair started falling out in clumps. But while it's an idea that seems plausible, it has no real basis in fact, says Catherine Chambliss, Ph.D., chair of the psychology department at Ursinus College in Collegeville, Pennsylvania.

Your hair falls out constantly, at a rate of 50 to 100 strands per day, regardless of stress levels. About 90 percent of your hair is growing at any given time; the remainder is in a resting phase that lasts 2 to 3 months. At the end of this resting stage, the hair is shed, replaced by a new hair from the same follicle, and the growth cycle begins again. Unless you have an inherited vulnerability to hair loss, like male pattern baldness, your shed rate is going to fall in this range. While some dermatologists think "catastrophic" stress—say, from a divorce or job loss—may cause certain people to lose a few extra strands, all agree that this hair grows back within a few weeks.

However, a scalp condition called alopecia may be stress responsive, says Dr. Chambliss, but the jury is still out. With alopecia, women lose hair on their heads in defined patches or, in some cases, completely. Since the cause of this ailment is unknown, it's impossible to say whether it is aggravated by stress, she says. If you're concerned about excessive hair loss, you should see a dermatologist. Another reason we may think stress causes hair loss is the saying "I'm going to pull my hair out (over this particular situation)." Of course, if you actually acted on this impulse, then you certainly could blame your hair loss on stress.

and their ways of perceiving the world as part and parcel of who and what they are.

The danger of episodic stress, says Gorkin, is that it sensitizes the body, triggering a hyper response to life's minor provocations. In short, episodic stress itself alters your ability to cope with stress, causing your body to produce too many excitatory chemicals or too few calming ones, he says. As a result, the biological response originally reserved for life-threatening events is turned on by traffic snarls and jammed copiers.

Episodic stress, and the extended overarousal that comes with it, can cause persistent tension headaches, migraines, hypertension, chest pain, and heart disease. People with episodic stress are commonly short-tempered, irritable, anxious, and tense.

Managing Episodic Stress

Treating episodic stress requires intervention on a number of levels, says Gorkin, and generally calls for professional help. Therapists need to be flexible and allow people to try different stress-reduction techniques, rather than cleave to a one-size-fits-all approach. Relaxation techniques often don't work when someone is hypersensitized to stress, but biofeedback, meditation, visualization, or taking up a hobby might work wonders. Just as everyone reacts differently to stress, everyone responds to different de-stressors, he says. However, Gorkin adds, everyone seems to benefit from "knowing your limits and

impatient, overly competitive, driven by some inner sense of perfection.

One major difference between episodic stress and acute stress is that sufferers are usually unaware of the problem. Their habits and personality traits may be so ingrained they can't imagine a lifestyle that isn't stress-filled. They see their lifestyle, their patterns of interacting with others, not limiting your no's—a key rule of safe stress."

Chronic Stress

Chronic stress is the most serious form of stress. This is the grinding stress that wears down people day after day, year after year, as overexposure to stress hormones wreaks havoc on mind and body.

It's the stress of poverty, of dysfunctional families, of being trapped in an unhappy marriage or a despised career. It's the stress of unrelenting demands and pressures. With chronic stress, a person cannot see a way out of a challenging situation; with no hope, they give up searching for solutions.

Sometimes traumatic experiences become internalized, making the individual more sensitive to stress. The worst aspect of chronic stress is that you get used to it. While acute stress is shocking, chronic stress is familiar, and as a result, sufferers almost never realize the effect it has on their lives. Chronic stress may express itself through suicide, violence, heart attack, stroke, and perhaps even cancer, says Jeremy Kisch, Ph.D., senior director of clinical education for the National Mental Health Association in Alexandria, Virginia. People wear down to a final, fatal breakdown because their physical and mental resources are depleted through long-term attrition.

The symptoms of chronic stress are treatable, he says, but may require extended mental health care, along with stress management and behavior modification.

ON THE FRONT LINES
A Female Firefighter

Imagine yourself in peaceful slumber. Suddenly, there's an ear-splitting alarm. In a flash, you pull on quilt-lined, fire-resistant pants, heavy boots, and a cumbersome coat, then swing behind the wheel of a ladder truck. As you weave through city traffic, two thoughts pound in your mind: "Someone's life could be in danger, so let's make the best time possible," and "We've got to get there safely without endangering anyone on the road."

At the scene, you'll probably have to maneuver this hulking vehicle down a narrow street, around gawkers and parked cars, praying to find the best spot in relation to the fire. Then you enter a burning building, not knowing what, or who, you might find. Welcome to the world of Gayle Unzicker, a fire apparatus operator for the city of Cincinnati.

Shifting from calm into full-blown disaster mode is a workaday reality for every firefighter. Yet even downtime for female firefighters is stressful, says Unzicker, "because being part of a minority introduces very definite psychological turmoil." A firefighter for 15 years, she enjoys the sense of mission: "It's like you get bitten by a 'bug'—you love it so much you'd do it for free." But the stress never goes away, she says. The firefighter's work life is characterized by extended periods of preparation, such as cleaning equipment and checking hydrants, interrupted by episodes of intense stress where performance demands mental and physical exertion near the limits of human endurance.

Adding to the strain of the job is the stress female firefighters put on themselves, she says. In this traditionally all-male environment, "women don't feel they have the latitude to make a mistake," she says. "All those man/woman issues never go away, and women feel like they have to be perfect just to be accepted."

Unzicker's lucky to have two other females in her firehouse, so she has someone to commiserate with during her 24-hours-on/48-hours-off shifts. "Just sharing those petty work annoyances with someone really helps," she says.

Stress-Control Tactics That Backfire

Just as every woman is unique, so, too, are the ways we choose to react to stress. Some of us yell at our kids; others tailgate the driver who cut us off, drink off a bad day or gamble away a weekend. We smoke to calm our nerves, oversleep to avoid the stressors, or toss and turn all night worrying about them. Maybe you mow the lawn at 7:00 A.M. to exact revenge on your neighbors for a late-night party. Or maybe you stand before the refrigerator, guiltily eating anything that helps you forget your pain.

At some point we've *all* acted in unhealthy ways as a result of stress. But for some, such actions can turn into self-destructive habits—the kind that ruin our health and relationships. Think of this chapter, then, as a warning, a yellow light—red if you recognize yourself in any of the descriptions. Then continue reading this book to learn specific, concrete ways you can manage and control your stress—before it controls you.

Why We Self-Destruct

Certainly no one's immune to *severe* stress, but individual temperaments—thanks to both na-

ture and nurture—account for whether you get as agitated over a broken toaster as another woman might get over a rained-out wedding.

Scientists have worked for years to find a way to predict which of us is most likely to flip out in a particular situation. That's where the whole Type A personality theory comes from. But it isn't just how tightly wound we are that determines our reaction to burnt toast or soggy wedding cake; it's our "sunny vs. rainy" view on life.

For instance, research shows that optimistic women are less distressed when coping with breast cancer than pessimistic women, says study author Charles Carver, Ph.D., professor of psychology at the University of Miami in Coral Gables, Florida. Not only did the more optimistic women put a better face on a bad situation, but they also accepted and learned to deal with the cancer more quickly than the pessimistic women.

Another plus: Optimists don't worry as much about what *might* happen.

They're more like the zebras in Robert M. Sapolsky's book *Why Zebras Don't Get Ulcers* who, although they know from experience that a lion is out there somewhere, graze unconcerned until it makes its appearance.

Other personality types also determine our reactions to stress. Impulsive women, for example, are more likely to be careless with their money and fall into debt. Novelty seekers are more prone to end up in military combat. Having a hostile personality ups the chances that we'll drink alcohol, which can increase our exposure to assault, traffic accidents, divorce, domestic violence, and employment problems.

How We Self-Destruct

Ironically, the things many of us do to feel better only make our problems worse. Binge eating, smoking and drinking, and overdoing tranquilizers eventually may make us fat or addicts, ruining our health and putting strain on personal relationships, says Michael McKee, Ph.D., vice chair of psychiatry and psychology at the Cleveland Clinic Foundation.

Consider these misnamed "stress relievers."

Food. Years of conditioning have taught us to crave certain foods, in particular sweets, when we're stressed. If Mom used to give us dark-chocolate nonpareils to cheer us up, we now associate that food with comfort. Not to mention the fact that chocolate contains the natural chemical theobromine, which can raise levels of the feel-good hormones known as endorphins.

The problem is that chocolate, cakes, cookies—even fat-free muffins—all contain a *lot* of processed sugar. And the more processed sugar we eat, the higher our blood sugar levels spike. As a result, we stop making natural glucose, so when the "sugar high" wears off, stress

STRESSING OUT WITH YOUR MORNING COFFEE

While many of us turn to coffee, tea, or chocolate to stay awake, few may know that the daily cup of java may also enhance our stress, sending our bodies into fight-or-flight mode. Caffeine raises levels of the stress hormones epinephrine and norepinephrine, which in turn elevate our heart rate, blood pressure, and adrenaline level. In some, caffeine even triggers panic attacks, episodes defined by intense anxiety, difficulty breathing, sweating, and rapid heartbeat. Experts agree that anyone suffering from panic attacks should gradually cut caffeine out of their diet completely. But even if you experience the less severe symptoms of irritability and restlessness, it's wise to limit yourself to a cup a day. Switch to a more calming drink, like chamomile tea, suggests Pamela Peeke, M.D., author of *Fight Fat after Forty* and assistant professor of medicine at the University of Maryland School of Medicine in College Park.

increases, in the form of anxiety, fatigue, depression, or general irritability. We subsequently scramble for another quick fix.

Sugary foods also increase our insulin levels, giving us "the appetite from hell," says Pamela Peeke, M.D., author of *Fight Fat after Forty* and assistant professor of medicine at the University of Maryland School in College Park. That's especially a problem when coupled with the stress hormone cortisol, which *also* fuels our appetite for carbohydrates and fat.

Furthermore, the food we do eat when angry, sad, or frustrated gets sent directly to our belly, deep beneath the abdominal wall. Here, fat looks and acts differently than fat anywhere else in the body, raising our risk for heart disease, cancer, and diabetes.

The solution, says Dr. Peeke, is to eat foods that don't increase cortisol or insulin levels, such as raw vegetables; fresh or dried fruits (unsweetened); protein, such as unsalted nuts, low-fat yogurt, or cheese; and high-fiber breads—all of which take the body longer to break down.

And exercise. A vigorous walk or jog also releases endorphins, which inhibit stress, while raising levels of serotonin, nature's Prozac. It also burns off some of that anxiety-fueling adrenaline. Over time, exercise even conditions the body so it's more difficult for stress to throw our systems out of whack, says Dr. McKee.

Smoking. You know the obvious reasons why smoking is bad for you, but did you also know smoking is a stress *enhancer*? While any nicotine addict might argue otherwise, studies show that heavy smoking (about 20 cigarettes a day) even raises the risk of anxiety disorders such as agoraphobia and panic attacks.

Likewise, other studies have shown that kicking the habit *reduces* stress. Researchers speculate that the relaxing effect you feel when you light up is really just a reversal of nicotine's withdrawal symptoms, which include tension and irritability.

Additional stress may come from the feeling that you're not in control. Smokers *know* the downsides of their habit, including the potential harm it inflicts on others around them. But they may feel helpless to do anything about it.

In short, going off nicotine may temporarily stress your body because of withdrawal, but you'll find that you're much more relaxed in the long run. To find the best method for quitting, which varies from person to person, talk to your doctor.

Alcohol. At certain doses, alcohol stimulates the release of stress hormones, such as corticos-

WOMAN TO WOMAN

She Stopped Drowning Fear in Beer

For more than a decade, Lois, a retired schoolteacher, was low on self-esteem but high on booze—a combination that proved nearly fatal. Today, with the help of Alcoholics Anonymous (AA) and a host of stress-busting habits, she conquers her demons—including a recent bout with cancer—sober. This is her story.

I had my first blackout at age 15. I'd started drinking in junior high, and with just a few drinks, I was already forgetting things. It should have been my first warning that I was destined for the life of my alcoholic parents, but I didn't heed it.

In college, after-class beers became a daily ritual. Part of me *needed* the wine, the beer, the shots of schnapps, to feel like part of the human race. I didn't dance well. I wasn't as pretty as some of my girlfriends. Drinking made me feel less inadequate.

But the party didn't end after graduation. The Sunday before my first day of teaching, I got drunk out of fear. What if the kids didn't like me? What if the other teachers could tell I didn't know what I was doing? I started my career with a hangover.

The next decade consisted of "geographical cures." From San Francisco to Reno, then Germany to Lake Tahoe. All the while, I drank. I could see that I wasn't happy no matter where I went, yet I couldn't pinpoint the problem.

terone. Chronic drinking also increases levels of adrenaline, the fight-or-flight hormone. This may explain why more than half of all violent crimes are committed when the offender has been drinking.

Women are especially vulnerable to intoxication since we have less of the stomach enzyme that digests alcohol. Glass for glass, we absorb 30 percent more alcohol than a man of similar weight.

And the problem is epidemic. More than 12

Then, when I was in my early thirties, my friends confronted me. Indignant, I denied their accusations, despite a drunk-driving accident. I lost a lot of friendships, which only added to my stress.

Finally, at age 33, I attended my first AA meeting, solely to prove to a friend that I did *not* have a problem. Those 2 years of sobriety were hard. Finally, the inevitable happened: I relapsed. I said hurtful things to my AA sponsor and to an old friend, then threatened to jump off the Golden Gate Bridge. The next day, my anxiety was back. I couldn't look people in the eyes; my hands were clammy. I realized things might not have been perfect during those 2 sober years, but they were a lot better than when I'd been drinking. I went back to AA.

This time was different. I became very active in AA. I wasn't there to get people off my back. I was there to get sober. I started to ask what other members did when they were stressed. I started swimming and running. I went to therapy, leaned on friends more, and developed a spiritual program that incorporates meditation. On stressful days in the classroom, I'd quietly say the Serenity Prayer or step out for a breather and let my teacher's aide take over.

Today I'm celebrating 28 years of sobriety! Even last year, after a breast cancer diagnosis, alcohol was the *last* thing on my mind. Thanks to AA, I've learned to stay in the present, not to worry about things I can't control, and to make each day count. To do that, I need to be sober.

million Americans have at least one symptom of alcoholism, and one out of three of us say that alcohol abuse has brought trouble into our homes.

The hard part is admitting that you have a problem. Once you do so, help is everywhere. The best first step is probably through the doors of a 12-step program, such as Alcoholics Anonymous. You can find such groups listed in the yellow pages.

Shopping. For some, the drug of choice is spending. Whether it's for themselves or others, pathological spenders invariably use money and possessions to hide from the pain of inadequacy, real or imagined, says Yvonne Kaye, Ph.D., a financial and spiritual bankruptcy counselor in North Wales, Pennsylvania, and author of *Credit, Cash and Co-Dependency*.

The woman who uses gifts to buy off those who are angry with her isn't dealing with her feelings and stress but is escaping her problems. Likewise, those who splurge on themselves may get a temporary high but afterward feel sick and guilty.

Still others are hoarders. They use their possessions as an antidote to low self-esteem and believe that the more they have, the better off they are. They let their possessions form their identity and seek comfort in knowing that inanimate objects can never leave them or let them down, says Dr. Kaye.

But money and possessions won't make you happy or relieve your stress. "When one's happiness is dependent on anything—a person, thing, or circumstance—outside oneself, it can be taken away and everything lost," says Dr. Kaye.

And chronic shopping "therapy" usually worsens stress in the long run by creating financial problems that add to the shame, guilt, rage, and confusion.

To break the cycle, Dr. Kaye suggests cutting up your credit cards, staying away from malls, tossing out catalogues as soon as they hit your mailbox, and seeking help from a nonjudgmental friend. Also, to help you identify patterns, write down everything you buy and how you were feeling when you bought it.

Personality. Some of us cope with stress in a

TAMING TECHNOSTRESS

How many times have you read articles saying that technology will make our lives easier? Reduce our stress? Don't believe it. Our beepers, cell phones, e-mail, and fax machines may make us more efficient, but they also force us to take on too much.

Michelle Weil, Ph.D. and Larry Rosen, Ph.D., coauthors of the book *TechnoStress*, call this phenomenon "multitasking madness." As technology enables us to take on more and more, our brains become overloaded. "We find ourselves unable to think clearly, and we become forgetful," says Dr. Weil, a psychologist and president of HumanWare, a consulting firm in Carlsbad, California, specializing in the psychology of technology. "The more we juggle, the less efficient we become at any one task." This, not surprisingly, *increases* stress and diminishes our sense of control.

While there's no question that technostress affects us during the day—a study found that employees of one Fortune 1,000 company, for instance, sent and received an average of 178 e-mails a day—it also follows us into our living rooms or bedrooms. Whether we're trying to understand "basic" electronic gadgets—"What *are* those 30 buttons on the TV remote control for?" "Why can't I program this stupid VCR!?"—or figure out why our PC keeps crashing, technostress hits home. According to Dr. Weil and Dr. Rosen, about 85 percent of us feel uncomfortable with technology.

Even e-mailing from home can cause stress.

What used to be a fun tool for keeping in touch with friends and family across the country has become, for some, a chore. Suddenly our nieces and nephews and Great-Aunt Betty are online, and we have another 20 messages to read and respond to. Personal e-mail is now one more thing to check off our growing to-do lists.

Similarly, surfing the Internet creates its own sort of stress. By spending entire evenings online, which happens to many Web addicts, we avoid the real world and drive a wedge between ourselves and our family and friends.

While there's no global solution to avoiding technostress, you can start by identifying what's causing *you* the most anxiety. If it's information overload, maybe you need to simply turn off the pagers, shut down your e-mail, unplug the TV, and take a hot bath. Temporarily stepping away can help keep you sane.

If your stress stems from technical frustration, Dr. Weil offers several solutions: First, before buying any new device, test the customer service line. Make sure the reps are accessible. Stick with tried-and-true companies, rather than startups, which might fold in a week.

Also, have a friend or family member who's more techno-savvy show you one or two features to help you feel productive immediately. Don't try to take on too much at once, or you'll get overwhelmed and dread the learning process.

The trick, says Dr. Weil, is to become the driver of technology, rather than letting technology drive you.

kind of Jekyll-and-Hyde manner, turning into an entirely different person when we're overwhelmed, says James Averill, Ph.D., professor of psychology at the University of Massachusetts at Amherst.

If you're in a position of power, for instance, you might yell at subordinates to blow off some steam. But if the only "power" you come close to is the button on your computer, your actions might be more passive aggressive, such as "misfiling" that report the boss is looking for.

If you're a perfectionist, you may become overly obsessed with getting everything done and put in ungodly hours at the office, while a more laid-back colleague may crank out sloppy work or feel so overwhelmed that she procrastinates and misses deadlines. Each response, however, leads to additional stress. The overachiever loses balance and becomes physically and mentally exhausted, while the underachiever gets her unacceptable work kicked back, creating lower self-esteem and tension with the boss, or even depression, says Dr. McKee.

Then there's anger, another notorious reaction to stress overload. And just as women are more prone to depression than men (who tend to drink and gamble away stress), we're also more likely to yell and complain when we're stressed, says Albert Ellis, Ph.D., psychologist and president of the Albert Ellis Institute in New York City.

In some ways, venting can be good. Voicing our frustrations with a supportive friend in an attempt to reach a solution to our problems can be a healthy exercise. But too often we vent in unproductive ways, such as insisting that people who frustrate us stop acting as they do, which only escalates our stress by further upsetting us and the person we're with.

Recognize yourself in any of these scenarios? Then read on. Part 4, "Finding the Calm," is packed with healthy alternatives for relieving stress.

Anxiously Awaiting Calm

Louise Lindsey of Virginia Beach was driving near home the day it happened: sweaty palms, pounding heart, blurred vision.

"The next thing I knew, I had to stop the car," says Louise, 46. "I felt like I was having a heart attack." She was whisked by ambulance to an emergency room, where she was later pronounced healthy. She had suffered not a heart attack, a doctor told her, but a panic attack. Louise is one of 19 million people in the United States with an anxiety disorder, medical illnesses that include panic attacks, phobias, post-traumatic stress disorder, obsessive-compulsive disorder, and generalized anxiety. A woman with an anxiety disorder isn't just bothered by the everyday worries and anxieties that needle us all; she's plagued by relentless symptoms that disrupt her life, making it impossible to work, drive, or simply enjoy the day without a torrent of fears and worries.

"She's aware it's irrational," says Jerilyn Ross, a licensed clinical social worker in Washington, D.C., and president of the Anxiety Disorders Association of America. "But she can't control her thoughts."

More than twice as many women as men suffer anxiety illnesses, with the exception of obsessive-compulsive disorder, which strikes both genders equally.

And while stress—a job change, marriage, or divorce—doesn't *cause* anxiety disorders, it may trigger an episode.

As you'll see below, basic treatment for most anxiety disorders is medication, a type of talk therapy called cognitive/behavioral therapy, or a combination of the two. However, you can take some natural steps, in addition to the tips here and throughout this book, to reduce and eliminate negative stress and minimize anxiety-related episodes.

Feeling Like You're Dying: Panic Attacks

Not every woman who endures a panic episode—utter terror arising out of nowhere—will develop repeated attacks. But up to 6 million Americans do.

Symptoms include pounding heart, chest pain, nausea, chills, sweating, trembling, feelings of unreality, and the fear of dying or losing control. They generally last a few minutes but can last up to 10 minutes.

Fearing another attack, sufferers may begin limiting their activities until sometimes they're virtual prisoners in their homes.

After her first attack, for instance, Louise Lindsey stopped driving or going to the mall or the grocery store.

The traditional treatment for panic attacks is antidepressant or anti-anxiety medications and cognitive behavioral therapy. A therapist educates the patient about her illness and teaches her to gradually confront, and thus lessen, the anxious thoughts and feelings.

For Louise, it took just a couple of months of therapy and anti-anxiety medication before she drove that infamous road alone, telling herself the entire time: "You're going to be okay. You've driven this way before. You're safe."

She recalls, "When I got to the other end, you would have thought I'd just won the World Series—hands in the air, dancing in my seat."

Crossing the Worry Line: Generalized Anxiety Disorder

There probably isn't a woman alive who hasn't lain awake nights worrying over *something*, be it her job, a child's report card, or the gray

---

WOMEN ASK WHY

How can I stop worrying so much?

We all worry sometimes. Worry alerts us to danger or to problems we need to face.

But millions of us worry too much, too often, even though we don't have a full-blown anxiety disorder.

We virtually train ourselves to worry, which only reinforces the habit. Worriers often feel vulnerable if they're *not* worrying.

I call this "persistent toxic worry." We don't need professional intervention—we're able to function from day to day—yet worry eats away at our psyche and our physical state.

In today's techno-sophisticated world, where many of us spend our days behind computer screens (often in our own homes), our "disconnect" from others puts us at increased risk for toxic worry. Research shows that the more isolated we feel, the more we tend to worry.

But we can change our worrying ways.

My most powerful treatment: Never worry alone. When you talk about your worries with a trusted friend, coworker, or relative, the toxicity dissipates. You find solutions; your concerns aren't so overwhelming.

Some other top solutions for controlling everyday worries:

Get the facts. Exaggerated worry is usually based on a lack of information or on misinformation.

Make a plan to solve the problem. Are you worried about finances, your job, your health? Set up a savings account, talk to your boss, get that yearly mammogram, or see your doctor. Don't be a passive victim.

Get regular doses of human contact. We need to feel connected.

Let the worry go. Chronic worriers have a difficult time doing this because they usually do just the opposite. They hold on as though worrying will fix the problem. It won't.

Expert consulted
Edward M. Hallowell, M.D.
Author of Worry: Hope and Help for a
Common Condition

hairs that sprout in her brush. So how do you know when you've crossed the worry line?

"If it's to the point where you're aware that it's irrational, you can't seem to stop, and you're making accommodations in your life for the anxiety, seek professional help," Ross says.

One of her patients, a happily married woman with well-adjusted children, stayed up nights worrying that her kids were going to get sick, her husband would lose his job, or she would die early, leaving her kids motherless. Her fears were irrational. Her husband was doing well at work. Her children were healthy, and she was also in good health. Her fears seemed to come out of nowhere and were unrelenting.

She had generalized anxiety disorder—GAD—diagnosed when worries flood you for 6 months or more and focus on at least two aspects of life. You may also have physical symptoms, including trembling, twitching, muscle tension, headaches, sweating, and nausea.

Women with GAD endure chronic, daily anxiety "that is grossly disproportionate to any real threat of danger or anything negative happening," says Ross. About 4 million people have GAD, which is linked to impaired social life and low ratings of life satisfaction.

Once Louise Lindsey entered therapy, she realized that in addition to panic attacks, she'd had GAD for years. She remembers worrying in school "above and beyond" the norm.

As an adult, she says, "It was always the feeling of 'something's going to happen.' It consumes every aspect of your life."

As with panic attacks, treatment includes an-

WOMAN TO WOMAN
She Was Phobic about Choking

Marie Callahan of Wilmington, Delaware, was so afraid of choking that for 17 years she couldn't eat solid food. Though she'd never choked on food, Marie felt a lump in her throat every time she tried to eat. At one point, the 5'1" wife and mom weighed 85 pounds. Then in February 2000, a psychiatrist gave a name to Marie's problem: phobia. Today Marie has her life back. This is her story.

I always loved to eat, but I never had a weight problem, never dieted. At 19, I married a wonderful man and later gave birth to a beautiful daughter.

At around age 30, though, life changed. I felt a lump in my throat when I tried to eat solid foods, as if I were going to choke. I felt panicky, too, with sweaty palms and racing heart. Sometimes I just wanted to bolt.

My doctors said nothing was physically wrong.

To avoid the feeling, I ate only soft foods, such as puddings, soup, ice cream, mashed potatoes, cottage cheese. I would cook for my family, then take my "safe" foods into the bedroom and eat alone, the television droning on as a distraction. Even then, I had to force down my meals.

My fears grew. I felt as though I would choke at the grocery store, in restaurants, in traffic. When my husband and I went to weddings or parties, I pushed around the food on my plate, cutting the meat but never eating—and hoping no one would notice. My husband worried about me, as did I.

tidepressant or anti-anxiety medications and therapy to help you refocus your thoughts.

Facing Your Fears: Phobias

Everyone is afraid of something: staying home alone at night, interviewing for a job, dating again after a divorce. Yet most of us confront our fears and move on.

Women with phobias can't move on. They avoid the task or issue altogether or suffer intense anxiety doing it. They may fear objects or

Then, in January 2000, I caught the flu. I missed 3 weeks of work and was exhausted. My doctor referred me to a psychiatrist, who told me I had a phobia, along with panic and obsessive-compulsive disorder and depression.

Finally, I had a diagnosis. The psychiatrist sent me to a licensed clinical social worker in Wilmington who specializes in cognitive behavioral therapy and in treating conditions like mine.

She explained that I have a disease, no different than a person with diabetes, and that there was a kind of faulty wiring in my brain.

Then she had me eat foods I feared—one at a time, in her office. The first week, when she pulled out a bag of bagel chips, I thought I was going to die. But amazingly, I crunched and swallowed. Next came pretzels, nuts, a fast-food hamburger. Before, while, and after I ate, we talked about my fears and about the fact that I was okay and wouldn't choke.

I had "homework," too. Each week, I incorporated these foods into my diet at home and talked myself through my fears. I also take a low-dose antidepressant.

And it's worked. I've gained weight and am able to eat in restaurants again. In July, my husband and I vacationed in Las Vegas. For the first time in years, I wasn't consumed by fear and anxiety.

My next hurdle: cheese steak.

situations, including dogs, insects, airplane flights, elevator rides, bridge or tunnel crossings. Or they may have a social phobia: a fear of being scrutinized or embarrassed in public, which makes them shy away from parties, making friends, walking down an aisle. Most common is a fear of public speaking.

Panic-like symptoms may accompany phobias, including heart palpitations, sweating, faintness, and shortness of breath.

Treatment includes a therapy called desensitization, which exposes you gradually to your fear. A woman afraid to drive over a bridge, for instance, may start by crossing smaller bridges with a friend in tow, says Constance Dancu, Ph.D., a cognitive behavioral therapist in Wilmington, Delaware. Eventually, she crosses higher bridges on her own.

Beyond the Ritual: Obsessive-Compulsive Disorder

Many of us follow daily rituals. One woman coordinates the clothes in her closet by color. Another checks that her iron is unplugged before leaving the house.

But some people—about 1 in 50—obsess to the point of illness. They are compelled to perform certain behaviors, such as scrubbing their hands or countertops hundreds of times or checking every 10 minutes that the stove is off or windows locked, all in a useless attempt to alleviate—at least for a while—their anxieties.

The disorder is diagnosed when obsessions and compulsions consume at least an hour a day, thereby disrupting daily life.

"Most common is the person who keeps driving back to the same spot again and again, convinced they hit someone," says David R. Spiegel, M.D., a psychiatrist in Chesapeake, Virginia.

Treatment includes antidepressant medication and a behavior therapy intervention called response prevention. "We expose them to the thing that's most dreaded and prevent the response," Dr. Spiegel says.

So the hand washer who fears germs may be asked to touch a doorknob, then kept from washing her hands afterward. She learns over time that no harm will come to her. The patient who fears that she hit someone with her car will realize she hurt no one.

After the Crisis: Post-Traumatic Stress Disorder

Once called battle fatigue, post-traumatic stress disorder (PTSD) is familiar to many as an illness suffered by war veterans.

But almost any terrifying incident can leave you "shell-shocked"—experiencing flashbacks from the event, feeling numb to your emotions, avoiding places that trigger memories. You may easily startle, sleep poorly, and feel depressed or detached. A diagnosis comes if the symptoms persist for a month or more.

Victims of rape, muggings, childhood sexual abuse, or horrific car accidents are among potential PTSD sufferers, says Dr. Dancu, coauthor of *Cognitive Behavioral Treatment for Adult Survivors of Childhood Trauma.*

Some women experience symptoms almost immediately. Others may develop PTSD months or even years after the incident, which is why Dr. Dancu cautions women who have experienced trauma not to quickly dismiss their feelings.

"A huge part of PTSD is avoidance," she says.

Genetics, repeated trauma, or preexisting illnesses like depression also increase your risk of PTSD, says Phebe Tucker, M.D., associate professor of psychiatry at the University of Oklahoma in Oklahoma City, who helped treat

WOMAN TO WOMAN
She Suffered Severe Trauma

Debra Puglisi Sharp was working in her garden on April 20, 1998, when her husband was killed by an intruder in their Newark, Delaware, home. Debra was then raped, kidnapped, and held hostage for 5 days. Today she suffers from post-traumatic stress disorder but is healing, one day at a time. Integral to her healing, she says, is talking about her trauma, on television, in newspapers, to groups. This is her story.

I lost my first husband one month shy of our 25th anniversary. He was shot and killed by a man who entered our home through the back as I tended my garden in the front yard.

I never heard the shot that took his life. But later, when I went inside, the intruder hit me, knocked me to the kitchen floor, bound my wrists and ankles with rope, and raped me. He left, but returned, covered me in a comforter from my bed, locked me in the trunk of his car, and took me to his home.

During the next 5 days, I was bound with rope and raped a half-dozen times. My captor was high on crack cocaine but stopped using the drug a few days after kidnapping me. I tried to befriend him, hoping my life would be spared.

In the meantime, my father and then-19-year-old twin son and daughter frantically wondered where I was; the police initially suspected me in my husband's killing, although my purse, car, and belongings had all been left behind. They soon realized I was also a victim.

Only during my capture did I learn my husband had died; I

survivors of the 1995 federal building bombing and a 1999 major tornado there.

Some studies indicate that trauma may actually change the brain's function or structure. For example, the hippocampus (where we process memories) is sometimes smaller in people with PTSD who were traumatized in childhood. However, it is not clear whether these differences occur as a result of trauma or whether they heard it during a radio report in the house where I was hostage.

On the fifth day, my captor switched the ropes to hand-cuffs on my wrists and ankles. That evening he went to work, and I was able to maneuver to a telephone and call 911. The police rescued me and arrested my captor on the nearby assembly line where he worked.

He was convicted and is serving 10 life sentences with no possibility of parole. (He later was also convicted of raping another woman.)

I attended my husband's viewing and funeral. At the viewing, a man I had dated 30 years before was among the hundreds to offer their condolences. In July 2000, this man would become my second husband.

I was referred to a cognitive behavioral therapist, who taught me to face my trauma. Part of that meant telling my story on tape and listening to it, which helped desensitize me and prepare me to testify in court and thus move past the pain.

I still experience occasional flashbacks, a hallmark of post-traumatic stress disorder. Initially I was simply numb. Sometimes, though, I vividly remember the experience; a few times I have relived it. I once stood outside the new home my husband and I now share, shaking, certain a stranger was inside.

I will always have this disorder. You cannot survive something like this and not have emotional pain.

But I carry on. I tell my story, believing that it will help others heal also.

predate trauma and may herald a vulnerability to PTSD, Dr. Tucker says.

Treatment includes antidepressants and other medications. Therapy involves exposing patients to memories of the trauma while teaching relaxation and coping techniques. Some of the bombing survivors in Oklahoma City, for instance, were gradually "desensitized" to trauma reminders to the point where they could visit the scene. Such exposure raises our ability "to gradually tolerate the environment or memory," Dr. Tucker says.

So a rape victim may relive the trauma in the safety of her therapist's office by closing her eyes and talking about it in detail while her account is recorded on tape. She then takes the tape home and listens. "It helps to process all the emotions associated with the assault or trauma," says Dr. Dancu.

"This technique is effective," she adds, "but you shouldn't try it without the support of a counselor."

Working It Out on Your Own

In addition to professional help, here are some things you can do on your own to cope with anxiety disorders.

Talk it out. This is particularly helpful when you find yourself confronted with anxiety-provoking situations, Dr. Dancu points out. You might say, "I know what's happening," "I'm okay," or "This is just a thought, a memory. It can't hurt me."

Work it out. Do something physical every other day, says Edward M. Hallowell, M.D., a psychiatrist in Sudbury, Massachusetts. Exercise dissipates the "background noise" and anxiety that build in our brains, he says.

Rest your brain. "A lot of my patients say that when they don't sleep well, the next day they have more panic attacks," Ross says. Sleep replenishes the body and mind. So get enough—as much as it takes for you to awaken without an alarm clock.

Eat wisely. "People with anxiety disorders have an exquisite sensitivity to their physiology," says Ross. They may misinterpret the light-headed or dizzy feeling associated with a drop in blood sugar level as an anxiety or panic attack.

Take a breather. Dr. Dancu prescribes a relaxing, cleansing breath. Inhale deeply from your belly. Silently repeat the word "calm," drawing out the *m* and exhaling to a count of 10. Repeat three or four times.

Relax. Dr. Dancu often suggests progressive muscle relaxation for patients with generalized anxiety. Close your eyes, breathing deeply from your belly. Tense and then relax your muscles one by one, from head to toe. Join a yoga class for a similar effect, says Ross.

Avoid alcohol. Women with anxiety disorders may self-medicate with alcohol, a potent relaxant, says Bernard Vittone, M.D., a psychiatrist in Washington, D.C. But when the relaxant wears off, they may become "hypersensitive" and suffer rebound anxiety. Some patients report a slew of panic attacks the day after drinking.

Curb caffeine. Coffee and other beverages and foods containing caffeine can bring on a panic attack, so try to steer clear of them, says Ross.

For more information on anxiety disorders, visit the Anxiety Disorders Association of America Web site at www.adaa.org or the National Institute of Mental Health site at www.nimh.nih.gov. You can contact these organizations for published information by writing to: Anxiety Disorders Association of America, 11900 Parklawn Drive, Suite 100, Rockville, MD 20852; and National Institute of Mental Health, Public Inquiries, 6001 Executive Boulevard, Room 8184, MSC 9663, Bethesda, MD 20892-9663.

PART TWO

To
Your
Health

Stress and Your Heart

Just after Christmas in 1995, Sylvia, then 57, an artist, reupholsterer, and furniture refinisher in Mountaintop, Pennsylvania, was upstairs in her rambling, rural two-story home when she felt a heavy weight on her chest, as if someone were sitting on her. Pain radiated down her left arm.

She'd felt unusually tired for a couple of days and had noticed uncharacteristically dark circles under her eyes. "I didn't pay much mind to it," she says. She thought it was fatigue from the holidays and the stress of life. Five of her immediate family members had died in the past 3 years, and she was now living in her family's home. Her fatigue, she figured, was simply a result of all that had been going on.

Until that late December day.

"All of a sudden this wave came over me," says Sylvia, now 62. She called downstairs to a friend: "I need help. I'm having a heart attack." Her friend drove her to the hospital, about 20 minutes away, where Sylvia spent the next 6 days, including 2 in intensive care.

She was fortunate. The damage wasn't severe, doctors told her, and she wouldn't need surgery.

Yet coronary heart disease, which causes heart attacks, is the leading cause of death for women in this country.

The most often cited risk factors are high blood pressure and high cholesterol, obesity, smoking, inactivity, diabetes, previous heart attack, family history, and, in postmenopausal women, loss of protective estrogen. And let's not forget stress, which Sylvia blames for her heart attack.

"Stress is a direct risk factor for heart disease, just like cholesterol and high blood pressure," says Alan Rozanski, M.D., a cardiologist and director of nuclear cardiology and cardiac stress testing at St. Luke's–Roosevelt Hospital in New York City. So reducing your risk of heart disease may be as simple as curbing your stress.

About Heart Disease

One of the heart's primary functions is to move the oxygen-rich blood from the lungs through the arteries, veins, and tiny capillaries that resemble a small-scale version of the interstate highway system. Healthy arteries are as strong and flexible as rubber bands. Inside, they are as smooth as glass to facilitate bloodflow. As we age, however, our arteries harden, narrow, and scar. Fat and cholesterol, or plaque, and calcium accumulate inside them, making their surfaces as bumpy as a dirt road after an ice storm. As the condition, called atherosclerosis, worsens, the hard outer shell of plaque may break apart and block an artery. A blood clot may then form, causing pain or a heart attack. Stress just makes the situation worse.

When we're anxious or tense, our bodies release stress hormones such as adrenaline, noradrenaline, and cortisol, which cause blood vessels to constrict and make heart rate and blood pressure rise. With chronic stress, blood pressure continues spiking and, over time, damages those artery walls, increasing the risk of heart disease.

Some studies show stress also raises cholesterol. Both short-term and long-term stress can increase LDL, or "bad," cholesterol, says Catherine M. Stoney, Ph.D., professor of psychology at Ohio State University at Columbus. She has studied cholesterol and psychological stress in men and women for more than a decade. As early as the 1950s, studies showed higher cholesterol levels in race-car drivers after competition. More recently, Dr. Stoney has shown that airline pilots studying for recertification exams had higher cholesterol levels in anticipation of the test.

Dr. Stoney also found that stress raises levels of homocysteine, an amino acid that researchers believe causes thickening and scarring of artery linings. In one study of 34 healthy women ages 40 to 63, she found that homocysteine levels

> ### HEART ATTACK FOR A WOMAN ONLY
>
> One reason that women may be more likely to die from heart attacks than men is because the signs can be so subtle.
>
> Instead of the classic radiating pain down the left arm that most men experience, the only warning sign we may have of an impending heart attack may be a vague sense that something isn't right, shortness of breath, dizziness, stomach pain, or belching, says William A. DeLacey, M.D., a cardiologist in Suffolk, Virginia, and a spokesman for the American Heart Association. Or, even more frightening, we may have no symptoms at all.
>
> Only our doctors can spot and help us control certain risk factors, such as high blood pressure and high cholesterol, which may be exacerbated by stress. If you have any concerns about your heart health, see your doctor for a complete physical.

rose when the women gave a speech before a camera or quickly subtracted backward by 13 (a researcher's way of creating stress). Afterward, their levels normalized.

You Say Stress, I Say Fun

Measuring stress is difficult, though. What is stressful to one woman may be another's motivator, Dr. Stoney notes. That's one reason the medical community has been slow to recognize stress as a major contributor to heart disease. Few large-scale studies have demonstrated that intervention methods to reduce stress also lower our risk.

From 1978 through 1983, Meyer Friedman, M.D., a cardiologist in San Francisco, studied 900 men and women identified as type A's, all of whom had previously experienced heart attacks. Dr. Friedman showed that behavior modification strategies—such as not wearing a watch, or thinking "lovely things" while waiting in line—

cut the number of heart attacks and sudden death among the group.

Today researchers are homing in on other aspects of personality or lifestyle. Mind-body researchers have pinpointed five psychosocial, or stress-related, factors that contribute to heart disease, says Redford B. Williams, M.D., a professor of psychiatry at Duke University in Durham, North Carolina, and coauthor of *Life-Skills*.

Hostility. Research shows that hostile people excrete more stress hormones in their urine than their calmer counterparts. One study of 77 healthy women found that those who scored high on hostility surveys had higher levels of LDL cholesterol. Other research shows surges in blood pressure in married couples asked to recall a recent argument.

Depression. In the United States and Denmark, studies found that healthy people who were depressed were more likely to suffer a heart attack 5 years after their depression hit than those who weren't depressed. In one study of people who had had heart attacks, about 16 percent of those who were also depressed died within 6 months of the heart attack, compared to 3 percent of nondepressed patients.

Low socioeconomic status. Research indicates that people with less education, a lower occupational status, a lower income, or a combination of the three—all stress factors—have a higher risk of coronary heart disease. Some studies show that people with low socioeco-

---

REAL-LIFE SCENARIO
She Can't Manage All of Her Stress

Cindy, 51, has had high blood pressure for most of her adult life but controls it just fine with the diuretic medication her doctor prescribed. But since she went through menopause, her blood pressure keeps spiking. She's eating right—lots of fresh vegetables and fruits and whole grains and breads. And she walks 3 miles several times a week. Lately, though, she's been under a lot of stress at work, where she is an accountant, and at home, where she and her husband are trying to work on a faltering marriage. And, while Cindy and her husband love their children, it's been tough trying to put all three through college. What should she do?

Cindy must first consult her physician, who should review her medical history. Her surges in blood pressure are of concern. We know that excess variability in blood pressure—even if it's not that elevated—is a risk factor for organ damage.

Plus, she already has one major risk factor for heart disease—her high blood pressure, or hypertension. Psychosocial factors, such as stress, combine with conventional risk factors to promote atherosclerosis, a buildup of plaque in the arteries that can lead to blockages and heart disease. So she's dealing with at least two major concerns.

Cindy also has work stress and a poor social situation. If

---

nomic status are twice as likely to die after a heart attack than affluent patients. While researchers are not sure why the risk for this group is greater, some speculate that other stress-related behaviors, such as smoking, are at play.

High job strain. Research shows that employees who feel high stress but who have little control over their jobs are at greater risk for developing high blood pressure and having a heart attack.

Social isolation. Women who report little social interaction secrete more of the stress horshe tries to solve all of those problems at the same time, she is only putting added pressure on herself.

So after Cindy consults with her doctor, the most important problem for her to address is her lack of social support—another stressor—while keeping her work situation steady. Studies show that social isolation is a major risk factor for heart problems. Cindy could join a woman's support group, where she'll build more social ties. She might also join a local YMCA or cardiac group, where she can exercise with other people. She should build every aspect of social support into her life that she can. That will give her a boost to deal with the marriage. Additionally, she, alone or with her husband, should seek professional counseling for their marriage.

Once that's dealt with, Cindy can tackle her work situation. Along the way, she should continue with her exercise and healthful eating, which help lower her risk for high blood pressure and heart disease.

Expert consulted
Alan Rozanski, M.D.
Cardiologist
Director of nuclear cardiology and cardiac
*   stress testing*
St. Luke's–Roosevelt Hospital
New York City

mone noradrenaline (which constricts blood vessels) than women who have greater support. "Research shows that social isolation is a major risk factor for cardiac events and mortality," Dr. Rozanski says.

Researchers are beginning to identify why these stressors—which often "cluster" in individuals—contribute to heart disease. One apparent reason is that the constant barrage of the stress hormones noradrenaline and cortisol may make blood "stickier" and quicker to clot. Blood pressure and cholesterol may rise as well, possibly damaging artery walls over time.

And stress may amplify standard risk factors—causing us to smoke more, eat more fatty fast foods, or neglect regular exercise.

Exercise. Exercise helps your heart pump more efficiently and boosts bloodflow and oxygen, which lowers blood pressure and artery-clogging cholesterol. One study found that women who walked briskly for 3 or more hours a week lowered their risk for heart disease as much as 40 percent.

Try yoga. Yoga and other relaxation techniques, such as deep belly breathing, reduce adrenaline secretion, heart rate, and blood pressure.

Make friends. In one study, people were divided into two groups and then pressed into arguing. One group had someone hold their arm or hand, while the other didn't have anyone touching them. Those with physical support fared better. "It's like a calming effect of the whole nervous system physiologically," Dr. Rozanski says.

Get a pet. Research shows pet owners have less depression and lower cholesterol and blood pressure than non–pet owners. Dog ownership in particular increased the likelihood of surviving a heart attack. Researchers speculate that this may be because pets offer unconditional love, and a beloved pet may motivate a seriously ill patient to stay alive.

Keep a journal. One study found drops in blood pressure and salivary cortisol among employees of a large organization who were randomly assigned to write about their emotions, says James W. Pennebaker, Ph.D., professor of psychology at the University of Texas at Austin. Simply sit down with a blank piece of paper and write nonstop about whatever is stressing you.

Stress and Your Stomach

Scarfing up fried jalapeño poppers and chasing them with tequila shots would wreak havoc on anyone's stomach for a night, but in times of stress, your gut can twist and turn and downright revolt for days at a time on nothing more than oatmeal and a banana.

Whether it's the everyday stressors of a rocky marriage, an unfulfilling job, or a troubled teen, or the occasional stressors of an accident, a daughter's wedding, or that big presentation at work, your gastrointestinal tract is as sensitive to what's going on outside it as a prowling watchdog.

"Stress can cause just plain abdominal discomfort," says Sandra Adamson Fryhofer, M.D., president of the American College of Physicians–American Society of Internal Medicine and practicing internist in Atlanta. "Diarrhea, cramping, and constipation are things I see quite frequently in my practice."

Even worse, stress can do such a number on your gastrointestinal tract that it may lead to more serious conditions. Yet you don't have to let stress take control of this most delicate system and become a real pain in the, ah . . . gut.

Untangling the Gut

The gastrointestinal (GI) tract involves more than just your belly. Food flows from your mouth, where enzyme-containing saliva begins to break down your food, down the esophagus to the stomach, where acids and enzymes break it down even more. From there, it travels through some 20 feet of small intestine, which extracts essential nutrients to send throughout your body, passing any waste through the large intestine (the colon) and on out of your body to greet the "porcelain goddess."

The liver, pancreas, and gallbladder lend their digestive help as well. So does the brain, believe it or not.

"There's a spider web of connections between your body, mind, life and all the reactions that run the cells of your body," says Donald Henderson, M.D., assistant clinical professor of medicine and gastroenterology at UCLA School of Medicine in Los Angeles.

"For instance, if someone put a cotton ball or a pin in the middle of your back, you'd know right away what it is without even seeing it, because you can get a sense from your skin. There are probably 10 billion nerve endings in the gastrointestinal tract that interrelate this same way to everything that goes on with us."

The gut actually has its own separate nervous system, called the enteric nervous system. What's more, that system is connected differently in each of us in terms of how we perceive and react to stress.

Think of digestion as an energy storage system designed for tranquility. We're wired not to digest food if we're under stress. When we perceive something as a stressor, our central and enteric nervous systems shift gears in order to save our lives.

"There's no sense in digesting food if you're going to die, so you might as well get out of that situation before you can digest food," explains Kayle Sandberg-Lewis, a stress management and biofeedback practitioner in Portland. "One of the first things that happens under stress is that the mouth goes dry because saliva's not needed to break down food."

Stress: When Your Gut Cries for Help

Whether your stress is daily, sporadic, or post-traumatic, it engages your gut in a war. The only difference is how long your GI complaints last.

Acute stress is when you experience something and then it's over. But chronic stress, which most of us suffer from, says Steven Sandberg-Lewis, N.D., a naturopathic physician and chair of the diagnostic sciences department at the National College of Naturopathic Medicine in Portland, Oregon, "is a whole different ball game."

"Instead of going back to normal digestive function, you stay in this chronic stress response," he says. "Your digestive function never

becomes optimal. That's when you get chronic digestive disorders."

Subliminal stressors can also affect digestion. For instance, if your parents criticized you or you fought with siblings during childhood meals, you've likely connected that distress with eating and digesting.

"Even if that parent or sibling isn't around anymore, you still have that same, dysfunctional digestion because you've learned that pattern," Dr. Sandberg-Lewis says. "You may have to go back and resolve some family issues before you can really get your symptoms under control."

Dr. Sandberg-Lewis once treated a client with ulcerative colitis who took five medications daily. "She was working in the family business, taking orders from her father, and it wasn't until she went back to school to do what she really wanted to do—write children's books—that she relieved the stressor that was literally eating her up."

Without such changes, here's where unchecked stress can lead.

Ulcers. Some 20 million Americans experience abdominal pains associated with peptic ulcers, accompanied by gnawing or burning pain between the navel and the bottom of the breastbone. Less common symptoms include nausea, vomiting, and loss of appetite. Duodenal ulcers—in the top part of the small intestine—typically strike between the ages of 30 and 50, while stomach ulcers, more common in women, typically hit after age 60. Both types are considered peptic ulcers, which are caused by digestive juices and stomach acid eating away at the intestinal or stomach lining.

Regular use of nonsteroidal anti-inflammatory drugs (NSAIDs), such as ibuprofen and aspirin, also can irritate the stomach lining and is the primary drug-related cause of ulcers.

Ulcers were once thought to be purely psychological. Then, in 1982, the bacterium *Heli-*

cobacter pylori was discovered, and doctors assumed that they could pin the entire blame for these gnawing, burning little sores on a germ. Two weeks of antibiotics, they thought, and no more ulcers. Recently, however, doctors are again looking at stress as a cause of some ulcers—a cause that may be compounded by the presence of *H. pylori*.

For example, various studies have shown that people who suffer from serious life trauma—whether earthquakes, economic crises, or war—are more likely to develop an ulcer within the next 9 to 15 years. Even rats develop ulcers when they're separated from their mothers too early.

The reason is that when you're under stress, acid production in the stomach shuts down—and takes with it the production of protective mucus. When you recover and eat, the acid comes back more quickly than the mucus. Then there's no mucosal wall to protect the stomach—and you can get an ulcer.

If the situation is neglected, stomach acid can eat a hole right through the intestinal lining, creating a trapdoor to bacteria, food, and digestive juices. Over time, repeated swelling and scarring may close the passageway from the stomach to the intestine. That's when surgery is likely.

Heartburn. Acid indigestion. Heartburn. Gastroesophageal reflux disease (GERD). They're all variations of a condition in which stomach acid does an about-face and flows back up the esophagus, causing a burning feeling in your chest and a bitter or sour taste in your mouth. Twenty-five million adults experience heartburn daily.

While stress isn't a direct cause of indigestion,

WOMEN ASK WHY

Why do some people who are infected with the H. pylori *bacterium* still not get ulcers?

Many people chronically infected with *H. pylori* never develop ulcers. This leads researchers to speculate that additional factors, such as genetic influence, may cause an infected person to develop a full-blown ulcer.

Still, researchers aren't certain what comes first: Does the infection cause an ulcer, or do people with ulcers just happen to make a nice home for the bacteria?

A joint study by researchers at Baylor College of Medicine in Houston and researchers in Sweden found that genetics does in fact play a hand in determining whether you're going to get ulcers. In other words, if your father had them, you might get them. But environmental influences play a larger role.

Researchers examined sets of twins reared together and apart and found that the kind of family life the twins had determined whether or not they developed an ulcer. The researchers speculate that those with the infection who got ulcers were part of a family that indulged in smoking and drank alcohol and coffee.

Some experts speculate that by increasing acid production, stress causes the proliferation of *H. pylori*, which live in

many people notice its symptoms more when they're under stress, says Dr. Fryhofer.

"Some of the habits we change when we're stressed—such as overeating, or eating right before bed—can exacerbate these symptoms," she says.

A tough day at the office bookended by a gridlocked commute isn't the only situation that causes stress.

Doctors at the Weill Medical College of Cornell University in New York City surveyed 2,000 heartburn sufferers to look at causes of heart-the protective mucous layer, because the bacteria can survive or even thrive in an acidic environment. And smoking can further break down the protective mucosal barrier, making it more likely that someone with *H. pylori* will get an ulcer. It could be compared to the wax layer on your car. If it breaks down, the paint will start to chip.

Additionally, there are different strains of *H. pylori* that may result in stomach or intestinal damage. Someone with a particularly aggressive strain of the bacterium may get an ulcer even if she's not stressed, say some researchers, while those with a more minor infection could get an ulcer because of severe stress, genetic influence, or use of NSAIDs.

Bottom line: We can no longer blame ulcers on *just H. Pylori* or stress.

Experts consulted
*Amy Foxx-Orienstein, D.O.
Chair of the Women in GI Committee of the
    American College of Gastroenterology
Associate professor of medicine
Medical College of Virginia
Richmond*

*Cynthia M. Yoshida, M.D.
Associate professor of gastroenterology and
    hepatology at the University of Virginia Digestive Health Center
Charlottesville*

burn. They found that women blamed their pain on stressful family situations 70 percent more often than men, and blamed a hectic day at home 55 percent more often than men.

Irritable bowel syndrome (IBS). This condition, also called spastic colon, results from abnormal function of the intestines. Symptoms include crampy abdominal pain, diarrhea and/or constipation, and bloating. It affects one in five Americans, mostly women, usually at times of stress. Because doctors don't know what causes IBS, there's no known cure. Treatment varies but includes many of the suggestions outlined in "De-Stressing Your Gut."

Inflammatory bowel disease. Inflammatory bowel disease (IBD) is an inflammation of the large intestine that can result in diarrhea, cramping abdominal pain, elevated white blood cell count, bleeding, and fever; the last three symptoms differentiate IBD from IBS. Similarly, however, doctors aren't sure what causes IBD. They suspect that it may be genetics or that antibodies "attack" the intestine. It manifests itself in the following two conditions.

Ulcerative colitis is an inflammation of the inner lining of the colon that may lead to chronic bleeding, diarrhea, and even anemia.

Crohn's disease is also an inflammation, but it penetrates deeper into the intestinal wall and can involve only the small intestine or both intestines. It may result in a narrowing of the small intestine.

While stress can make both conditions worse, there's no evidence that it *causes* either. Traditional therapies include prescription drugs, but a well-balanced diet low in roughage (as in veggies, fruits, and grains) and lactase can sometimes help.

De-Stressing Your Gut

Overall relaxation can help alleviate many gastric complaints, but see your doctor if your symptoms don't improve or if you take over-the-counter remedies more than twice a week. Left untreated, GI problems can become much worse. Something as seemingly minor as acid indigestion, for instance, can lead to severe chest pain, a narrow esophagus, bleeding, or even a premalignant condition of the esophagus—all of which may result in surgery.

In addition to the relaxation techniques described in part 4 of this book, there are specific things you can do to alleviate stress-related GI symptoms.

Drink up. Have at least six to eight glasses of water daily, says Dr. Sandberg-Lewis. "The mucus that's produced in the stomach is at least 95 percent water. Without water, you can't make enough protective mucus."

Check those acid levels. "Most people only think about too much stomach acid," says Dr. Sandberg-Lewis. "But too little or no stomach acid at all is extremely common." He says that at least half of those over 50 don't make enough stomach acid yet may still have reflux disease, heartburn, and similar symptoms. In this case, the burning occurs because, without an adequate amount of stomach acid (needed for the stomach to empty), their stomachs feel full for hours.

If your indigestion is worse while you're eating or for 2 hours after a meal, it may be due to low acid, he says. Try drinking 1 to 2 teaspoons of apple cider vinegar (to help the acid production) mixed with water just before you eat.

Get connected. "The biggest key is to be connected to the relationship between your symptoms and what's going on in your life," says Dr. Henderson. "Pay attention to the lesson that your history's taught you in terms of how your body reacts to stress so you can refocus and react differently."

So, if the last time you prepared a holiday

DE-STRESSING PLACES
The Orient

Our surroundings powerfully affect what we attract into our lives, says Carol M. Olmstead, a certified feng shui practitioner in Bethesda, Maryland. Using feng shui (pronounced "fung shway"), a system for arranging your surroundings in harmony and balance, she tries to balance or unblock your qi (pronounced "chee")—the harmonious flow of energy through your body—to positively affect prosperity, health, and relationships.

"Think of feng shui as acupuncture for your home—unblocking the flow of positive energy, removing negative energy, and allowing you to achieve your goals," she says.

To see how it works, take a look at the sacred space public relations account manager Fiona Beckman created in her London home. She took a tiny, junk-filled room and transformed it into her "creative room."

"She made the right choice," says Olmstead. "Clutter and items that have unhappy memories attached to them or that you simply don't like or no longer use carry negative energy known as *sha chi*, which represents stuck energy. Cracks, holes, broken or dirty items, peeling paint or wallpaper, and dead plants also represent *sha chi* since they block the flow of positive energy around you."

After the room had been professionally plastered, Beckman painted the walls bright orange and yellow up to the level of a shelf that circles the room at the top-of-the-door height. She painted the wall above the shelf and the

meal for 20, you ended up unable to eat because you developed a sour stomach, don't let that situation repeat this year. If you start feeling overwhelmed, ask for help with the shopping or in the kitchen—or plan ahead and make it a potluck meal.

Sit while eating. It'll not only benefit your GI tract; it also provides a chance to unwind.

Eat regularly. Don't skip meals or pile food on your plate at one sitting, especially if you have bottom of the shelf sky blue and attached glow-in-the-dark stars that match the handmade mobile hanging from the ceiling.

In feng shui, yellow is the color of the sun, so Beckman's choice of this color represents cheer and physical and emotional warmth, as well as brightening the room and elevating mental activity, says Olmstead. Blue, the color of water, represents flow and movement.

Beckman hung crystals at the west-facing window to catch the setting sun and put pots of herbs on the windowsill.

"Crystals are used in feng shui to circulate energy," says Olmstead. They can be used to enhance a positive situation. And the herbs connect Beckman to the natural world.

A small CD player in Beckman's room plays meditative and calming music, and a sound machine plays rain, sea, or waterfall sounds.

In feng shui, sound connects us to others in our environment and supports creativity, says Olmstead. "Music is a powerful way to uplift the chi in any environment and can soothe stressful home or office situations," says Olmstead.

Says Beckman, "I use the room just to chill out, to meditate, and for reading, drawing, painting—anything creative. That is its sole purpose, except for being a place the cats have adopted to sleep in."

And that's good, says Olmstead, since pets surround us with lively energy. But they should still have their own space in the home, she says.

Beckman is thrilled with her new room. "It's a haven from the stresses of the day at work."

IBS or ulcers. "Eat smaller quantities, particularly during stressful times," suggests Dr. Henderson.

Slow down. "Chew your food completely," adds Dr. Sandberg-Lewis. "There's an old naturopathic saying: 'Drink what you chew.' Really enjoy your meals, making mealtime a sacred time. Try to avoid eating if there's going to be something stressful going on."

Think about your typical meal: Is the television or radio on? Are the kids fighting? Is it the only time to catch up with your husband? Are you reading, or even driving?

"Don't try to do anything like serious digestion if you're in any situation where you don't feel confident," he says. Dr. Sandberg-Lewis recommends eating after a lunch meeting instead of during it or, if that's not possible, just picking at a salad. He also suggests eating fruit, vegetables, miso soup, or a soy-based smoothie if you schedule work-related meals. Just avoid the steak and pasta Alfredo.

Watch what you eat. Avoid coffee and greasy or spicy foods, as they contribute to acid indigestion. Alcohol can also delay an ulcer's healing time.

"Although you think you need coffee to wake you up, don't do it," says Dr. Henderson. The combination of stress and caffeine actually heightens the sensitivity of your nerve endings, which in the end can make you more jittery.

While diet has little to do with ulcers, doctors do recommend staying away from foods you've found to cause *your* symptoms to flare up. For more on a stress-reducing diet, see "The Anti-stress Diet" on page 138.

De-gas your diet. Beans, onions, broccoli, cabbage, bran, and cruciferous vegetables (such as broccoli and cauliflower) are just a few of the known gas-producing foods. Limiting or avoiding them may reduce IBS symptoms.

Try lactose-free. Up to 40 percent of IBS suffers are unable to digest milk sugar (lactose). In that case, opt for one of several brands of lactose-free milk on the market, or try one of the many calcium-fortified milk alternatives, such as soy or rice.

THE ANCIENT HEALING ART OF AYURVEDA

The ancient texts of Ayurveda, the early medicine of India, depict the relationship between imbalances in the nervous system and digestive disorders. The most important imbalances related to stress involve *vata* disorders of the nervous system, says Jay Glaser, M.D., medical director at Maharishi Ayur-Veda Medical Center in Lancaster, Massachusetts.

"*Vata*, which means 'movement,' regulates movement in the gastrointestinal, nervous, musculoskeletal, and genitourinary systems," he explains. "As movement, *vata* is like wind. When movement becomes aggravated from overuse, instead of producing effortless movement and elimination, *vata* makes the body take on the qualities of something left out in the wind: dryness, stiffness, brittleness, and irregular movement."

This is usually experienced on two levels. *Prana vata* is the aggravated movement of mind, intellect, and senses, as in too many unwanted or unnecessary thoughts. *Vyana vata* is the aggravated movement of the autonomic nervous system, including circulation and energy. It involves everything that is part of the stress response, such as heart palpitations, high blood pressure, fatigue, and insomnia.

This aggravation in the nervous system is tightly knit with aggravation of *samana vata*, which is "the wind that fans the flames of the digestive fires," says Dr. Glaser. When the "digestive fires" take on the aggravated movement, the upper digestive system becomes distressed—ergo bloating, gas, sluggish digestion, a feeling of heaviness after meals, even what was once referred to as nervous stomach.

"As a result of inefficient upper digestion, *ama*—residues of inefficient digestion—is created. *Ama* is heavy, and it loads the lower digestive tract and lodges in the tissues, where it becomes dried out by *vata*," says Dr. Glaser. We then experience constipation, lower digestive gas, and symptoms of irritable bowel.

Pacifying *vata* is usually accomplished by a physician trained in these procedures, but Dr. Glaser says there are many techniques that can be done at home "to reestablish the digestive fire."

Sip ginger water. Boil 2 teaspoons of fresh ginger in 1 quart of water for 5 minutes. Keep it in a thermos, and sip it throughout the day, especially

---

Nix the nicotine. Tobacco not only causes the stomach to make more acid, it also relaxes the barrier muscle between the stomach and the esophagus—and a weaker muscle lets more acid back up. Smoking also sends bile into the stomach, making the reflux nastier. Finally, smoking can both slow down the healing time for an ulcer and lead to a reoccurrence.

Slim down. It's sometimes tough to exercise or eat right when you're stressed, but if you're overweight, dropping a few pounds may help general gastric conditions and reduce heartburn. Excess weight puts extra pressure on your stomach and diaphragm, forcing open the lower esophageal sphincter and allowing stomach acids to back up into your esophagus.

Catch some Zzzs. A lack of sleep raises levels of the stress hormone cortisol and impairs your immune system.

Also, to keep your stomach acid where it belongs, try raising the head of your bed. Nail two jar lids, tops down, to a 4- by 4-inch piece of wood. The lids should be spaced far enough apart so that each leg at the head of your bed can rest in one. Or slide a 6- to 10-inch-thick foam wedge under your mattress.

when you're feeling out of balance, anxious, or tense.

Add some spice. Fresh digestive spices, such as cumin, ginger, turmeric, or cilantro (or coriander powder), can be added in moderation to cooked vegetables or dal (a thick soup of legumes). Well-cooked whole green or split yellow mung beans or small red lentils don't create gas, unlike most other legumes, says Dr. Glaser. If you have heartburn, GERD, or other hyperacidic conditions, cumin should be added only in small amounts to the hot cooking oil you're using to prepare your meal and should never be used in supplement form or as a powder. If you have dyspepsia—poor digestion in the upper GI area, usually associated with hyper-acidity—avoid coriander powder.

One of the most important spices for reducing gas and bloating is a plant resin called asafetida. It gives a delightful garliclike taste to savory dishes, but because it's pungent, use it only in extremely small amounts—just a few grains—in vegetable dishes or dal. You can find asafetida at an Indian food store, where it goes by the name *hingu*.

Shake it up. Sip lassi after lunch to aid digestion and replace good bacteria. To make it, blend 1 ta-blespoon yogurt, 1 cup water, a pinch of salt, and a pinch of cumin. People with IBS symptoms as well as those with gas and bloating problems can use lassi, but not people with dyspepsia. If you have acid trouble, the lassi can help when taken in small amounts.

Sip it. Make a cumin tea by boiling 1 teaspoon of cumin seeds in 1 cup of water for 5 minutes and sip it in the evening.

Steer clear. If you're having digestive difficulties, Dr. Glaser suggests avoiding frozen, canned, and deep-fried foods, leftovers, and yogurt by itself. (He explains, "As lassi it's light, but by itself it's heavy.")

Drink warm liquids. Drink milk only after it's boiled, preferably with a little fresh ginger root, and never right out of the fridge with other foods. Sip hot water before and during a meal. Never drink ice water, as it puts out the digestive fire.

Think balance. Eat heavier foods, those high in fat and protein, at lunch because they require a strong digestive fire: meat, fish, heavy cheeses, pasta, heavy breads, eggs, and even salads. For supper, eat lighter meals of soup, steamed veggies, and couscous.

Time yourself. Even if your sleep schedule is haywire from stress, don't eat later than 2 to 3 hours before bedtime. More than 40 percent of women say they get heartburn if they do.

Try biofeedback. Sandberg-Lewis recommends training with a biofeedback practitioner so you can learn to breathe through your nose, using your diaphragm. Nerve systems pass through the diaphragm, so this actually stretches out the diaphragm, making deep abdominal breathing easier, which in turn allows you to relax. A biofeedback specialist will also check whether you're unconsciously holding your breath or inhaling through your mouth and swallowing air as a result—which contributes to bloating and gas.

Loosen up. More than 20 percent of women recognize that wearing tight clothes around the belly not only feels uncomfortable but also may lead to heartburn. We're not just talking about those tight jeans you should've left in the 1980s. Snug elastic waistbands, panty hose, and girdles can all lead to discomfort.

Laugh a little. In addition to laughter's role as a proven stress reducer, studies find that its effects mimic those of aerobic activity. "Even if you fake-laugh for a couple of minutes, your heart rate will go up and your circulation will improve," says Karyn Buxman, R.N., a stress management consultant in Hannibal, Missouri, and author of *This Won't Hurt a Bit!*. Laughter also has a massaging effect on the internal organs.

Get a massage. A massage might be just what the doctor ordered when you're tense, but it can aid your digestion as well. Your upper GI connects to the thoracic area of your spine (from your shoulder blades through your ribs), and your lower GI connects to the lumbar region (the small of your back).

"We were told in school that the best compliment someone could give is if they passed gas during a massage," adds Sandberg-Lewis, who is a licensed massage therapist.

Try licorice. The natural supplement deglycyrrhizinated licorice, or DGL, a licorice extract, can help heal the stomach lining in cases of ulcers or gastritis—even GERD. It can also help produce a protective mucus layer in the stomach and reduce the number of *H. pylori* bacteria. You can eat it as a chewable tablet or take it as a capsule, says Dr. Sandberg-Lewis. Standard amounts are one or two 400–500 milligram tablets, taken at the beginning of meals.

Sample the stinking rose. Fresh garlic can reduce levels of *H. pylori* and may be extremely helpful when dealing with ulcers, says Dr. Sandberg-Lewis. Two cloves of raw garlic or a 1,000-milligram deodorized capsule, as long as it's not allicin-free, will do the trick.

But don't add extra garlic to your diet if you have heartburn or GERD, are taking medications to lower your blood sugar or thin your blood, or will be having surgery in the next 2 days.

Go with glutamine. The amino acid supplement glutamine is effective for Crohn's disease, ulcerative colitis, and ulcers, says Sandberg-Lewis. "It's a major nutrient for the cells lining the intestinal tract, and it helps heal the lining." He uses a powder with 3,000 milligrams per teaspoon and recommends 1 to 3 teaspoons each day, mixed with juice. But if you have kidney or liver problems, check with your doctor first.

Tipple tryptophan. Research in the Netherlands found that drinking a whey protein rich in the amino acid tryptophan increased levels of the feel-good brain chemical serotonin and reduced levels of the stress hormone cortisol, as well as the incidence of depression.

Look for whey supplements or powders at health food stores. But because the long-term effects of taking tryptophan aren't known and because tryptophan decreases your antioxidant levels (and could therefore encourage certain diseases), consult your doctor before taking it. The researchers note that a high-carbohydrate, low-protein diet may produce similar, serotonin-increasing effects.

Say no to NSAIDs. If you have an ulcer, gastritis, or GERD, stay clear of pain remedies like aspirin, ibuprofen, or acetaminophen, and talk to your doctor about other alternatives. A recent study examining more than 8,000 arthritis sufferers found that those who took the pain reliever celecoxib (Celebrex), a COX-2 inhibitor, had more than two-thirds fewer ulcers and ulcer complications than those who took ibuprofen or other NSAIDs.

Stress and Your Hormones

Nearly every system in our bodies is controlled by hormones. From estrogen to insulin, serotonin to cortisol, these critical chemical messengers determine the state of our physical and emotional health. When things are calm, they work like the proverbial well-oiled machine. But throw chronic stress into the mix, and it's like tossing a pile of rocks into that machine.

For example, the so-called stress hormones, which include adrenaline and cortisol, can affect the amount of sex hormones, such as estrogen and progesterone, we produce, creating problems in the reproductive system, says Saralyn Mark, M.D., assistant clinical professor of medicine at the Yale University school of medicine.

Hormones also may play a role in the fact that stress seems to be a greater problem for women than for men. Not only do we report higher levels of stress and more depression and anxiety than men, but our nervous systems tend to react more to stress than men's, possibly setting us up for greater health consequences. Experts are still researching all the reasons behind this gender difference, Mark says.

Hormones and Homeostasis

Hormones are highly specific agents released when a gland receives a signal from another part of the body that a hormone is required. For example, stress hormones are released when the nervous system detects a potential threat—anything from a charging tiger to a nasty coworker. These hormones can then trigger—or interfere with—the release of other hormones from other parts of the body.

When your body is functioning normally, it's in a state of homeostasis, or balance, with all systems working to maintain that balance. Chronic stress destroys that homeostasis by keeping levels of stress hormones high—which in turn creates imbalances in other hormone levels. For instance, stress affects insulin and thus blood sugar. Additionally, stress—or, more precisely, stress hormones—can create problems in your bones, muscles, and connective tissue. In fact, chronic stress, which results in chronically elevated levels of stress hormones, has been linked to osteoporosis and serious loss of muscle, says Pamela M. Peeke, M.D., assistant clinical professor of medicine at the University of Maryland School of Medicine and author of *Fight Fat after Forty*.

Two areas that are particularly important to women—reproduction and metabolism—are regulated by hormones that are especially sensitive to stress.

Stress and Reproduction

While the effects of stress on estrogen and the other sex hormones aren't yet fully understood, researchers know that stress can have a debilitating effect on reproductive health, making it harder for us to conceive by causing erratic menstruation or even the cessation of menstruation altogether. For example, "we know that women who eat poor diets and are socially isolated—two forms of stress—have less regular cycles," says Sarah Gehlert, Ph.D., associate professor at the University of Chicago School of Social Service Administration and the graduate program in health administration and policy.

One theory suggests that chronic stress reduces the amount of estrogen in your body. In addition to affecting the menstrual cycle, lower levels of estrogen may rob you of many of the hormone's protective effects on bones, the heart, and even your emotional health.

The ability of chronic stress to compromise fertility seems to be an evolutionary effect, says Dr. Mark. "If you're starving or living without adequate shelter or being chased constantly by wild animals, that's definitely not a good time to get pregnant."

But the effects of stress on sex hormones and reproductive health are perhaps most dramatic once pregnancy is under way. In one study, researchers found that female primates with a low social standing (a form of stress) have lower re-

productive rates, mature at a later date, and, when they do conceive, are more likely to suffer miscarriage or stillbirth.

Studies in women have found that those exposed to severe stress—that is, stress over an extended period of time or from an intensely stressful situation—while pregnant have a greater chance of delivering babies early or with birth defects.

Marjorie Sable, Dr.P.H., associate professor of social work at the University of Missouri–Columbia, also found that the babies of women who have a high level of perceived stress when pregnant are more likely to have very low birth weights—the condition most often associated with infant mortality. Again, researchers are still working out the exact mechanism at work here, says Dr. Mark, but stress appears to impede the actions of the hormones required to sustain a pregnancy.

While it's not known whether stress can accelerate the onset of menopause, researchers find that women who are experiencing stress report more frequent and more severe menopausal symptoms, perhaps because of unusually low estrogen levels. In fact, long before the onset of "the change," stress in perimenopausal women has been shown to trigger the same dramatic estrogen drop that is associated with the elevated risk of heart disease that women face after menopause.

Stress and Metabolism

Stress—and the hormones it produces—also can inhibit our ability to process the foods we eat. Many of the stress-induced problems involving metabolism are created by the actions of stress hormones, both on their own and through their effects on the hormone insulin. Insulin helps push glucose, the body's primary source of fuel, and amino acids, required to build muscle and other tissues, into cells.

When we're stressed, the stress hormones cortisol and corticosterone increase glucose levels in the blood and liver. This occurs because the body is attempting to mobilize its resources, making available all the quick-burning fuel it can. But after a while, this exaggerated glucose synthesis can create real problems as the body continually produces more insulin to push the glucose into cells. Eventually, the cells may become resistant to insulin's shepherding actions, resulting in high levels of glucose in the blood and possibly leading to diabetes.

Additionally, physical stress, such as an infection, makes it more difficult for those who already have diabetes to manage their disease, says Lynne M. Kirk, M.D., professor of internal medicine at the University of Texas Southwestern Medical School and spokesperson for the American College of Physicians in Dallas. This is true not only because of the effects stress hormones have on insulin but also because people who aren't stressed are generally better at maintaining the tight regimen of blood glucose monitoring and insulin injections required to control diabetes and prevent complications.

Stress also affects how we metabolize fat, and research suggests that chronic stress causes us to develop dangerous levels of fat, says Dr. Peeke. And it's not just any fat that develops, but fat deep within the belly; this leads to central, or

NEVER TOO YOUNG?

In addition to the crises and cares that plague you today, all the stress you've endured in the past also can affect your health.

For example, women with a history of depression or those who were abused as children typically have a much lower tolerance for stress as adults. One study found that this type of stress can make you hypersensitive to milder, day-to-day stresses. In fact, women in the study had stress hormone levels as much as six times the levels of women without a history of abuse or depression.

Other research suggests that stress encountered as early as birth can predispose you to a lifetime of hyperresponsiveness. Babies born via assisted vaginal delivery (which includes the use of forceps or other possibly painful interventions) cry more and have higher levels of stress hormones when they receive their first round of vaccines than those who came into the world via cesarean section. The same thing occurs in babies who have been circumcised.

"Studies are showing that there is a definite impact of childhood adversity on adult health," says Sarah Gehlert, Ph.D., associate professor at the University of Chicago School of Social Serivce Administration. "In a way, it's as if your body remembers stresses and anticipates them for the rest of your life. While stress-reduction techniques are effective in helping women cope with stress, there is no evidence yet that they reverse any effects of childhood stress."

visceral, obesity. "Unlike any other kind of fat, this is directly linked to heart disease, diabetes, and cancer," Dr. Peeke says. "And these particular fat cells are especially sensitive to stress hormones, meaning that the extra calories you consume when you're stressed go directly to these cells. And they can be lethal." A woman doesn't have to be obese to have this kind of fat, Dr. Peeke adds. "Lots of times, a woman will be of average weight and just carry some extra around the middle," she says. "She's more of an apple shape than an hourglass."

So when you're stressed, consider the following.

- ✦ When your stress hormones are high, you'll automatically crave carbohydrates and fat because those are the body's first choices to fuel its fight-or-flight response.
- ✦ Eating excessive carbohydrates and fat means you'll gain weight, with those same stress hormones now ensuring that the extra calories go to the fat cells in your belly.
- ✦ Eating a lot of carbohydrates immediately elevates levels of insulin in your bloodstream—and insulin is among the most powerful appetite stimulants the body makes.

Thus, when you're stressed, avoid cake and cookies, and opt for fresh fruit, whole grains, low-fat protein such as fish, chicken, or beans, and other healthy fare. "It's the combination of high-quality protein and carbohydrate that cuts the cravings for sweets and fats," says Dr. Peeke.

Although scientists are still investigating the connection between stress hormones and fat, some studies suggest that stress hormones may interfere with the body's ability to utilize leptin, a hormone that tells us when we're full. In laboratory experiments, rats with elevated levels of stress hormones overate and quickly became obese. When their stress hormone levels dropped, their appetites—and weight—returned to normal.

Stress and Immunity

Even before Hippocrates' time, in 400 B.C., medical care providers believed that "the passions" played some role in causing illness. Today they suspect that the immune system's natural tendency to take a hiatus during stressful periods may be left over from the days when stress was acute and external, as when a hungry lion decided you were dinner.

"It was adaptive to temporarily divert energy away from the immune system to the brain and muscles in order to respond to the stressful situation—when running from a lion, it's more essential to have energy than to fight off bacteria," says Christopher Coe, Ph.D., professor of psychology at the University of Wisconsin–Madison.

But today this system is far from perfect. Stressors don't go away as quickly as a sprinting lion, resulting in long-term suppression of the immune system, says Dr. Coe.

A Crash Course in the Immune System

Entire books have been written and entire careers focused on the immune system. But here are the basics: the soldiers (immune cells) move from their barracks (lymph nodes, bone marrow, spleen, thymus) through the body's roadways (lymphatic ducts and blood vessels) to patrol nearly all the body's organs in search of enemy bacteria, virus, parasites, or cancer. The soldiers can differentiate between your normal body's cells ("self") and enemy cells ("nonself"). Under normal circumstance, if they find an enemy (like bacteria), they attack it; and if they bump into one of your own cells (like a muscle cell), they move on.

This all works quite well when we're not stressed. There are several types of immune cells (all of which are white blood cells): B cells, T cells, and NK (natural killer) cells. The B cells make antibodies to fight infection, the T cells help to distinguish self from nonself cells, and the NK cells fight cancer cells. Another group of white blood cells, phagocytes, helps destroy invader cells and assist in controlling inflammation.

But the immune system isn't flawless, and sometimes it misses invaders, which is why we get sick. Sometimes it mistakes the body's own cells for invaders and attacks them, which is why instance, say you narrowly escape a car accident. When you see the car coming at you, the "fight or flight" response kicks in and your adrenal glands (located on top of your kidneys) release the stress hormone cortisol. Cortisol prepares your body to deal with the stress—immune cell soldiers prepare to fight, blood sugar rushes to the muscles to give them energy, breathing and heart rates quicken, and blood pressure rises. Cortisol also then helps *undo* the stress-preparing actions after the car misses you by inches.

We have some cortisol in our bodies at all times, even when we're not stressed (levels are high in the morning, and they steadily decrease throughout the day). But when stressors don't decline after a few minutes, as with chronic marital tension, the cortisol curve changes. The morning peak is absent or much lower, and overall levels are higher. Too much cortisol for too long suppresses the immune system. In HIV patients, for instance, it has been found that an increase in cortisol in the blood nearly doubles the risk that the patients will progress to full-blown AIDS.

Factors in the Stress–Immunity Equation

we get autoimmune diseases. Stress often acts as a catalyst in both these scenarios, lowering the number of B, T, or NK cells.

Stress sets off a chain reaction in the body. For

The stress-immunity equation is hardly so clear-cut, however. Multiple factors determine our own reactions, from genetics to the number of stress triggers in our lives, to the ways we deal with illness. Others include the following.

The type of stress you have.
Your boss comes in and fires you, then says, "April fool!" You laugh shakily, but the hairs on your arms are standing upright and your legs are wobbly. In a few minutes, however, you're fine. This is acute stress. But if you hate your job and for the past year you've been coming home with a tension headache, that's chronic, or prolonged stress, from which you may not recover so quickly.

"Prolonged stress decreases nearly all aspects of immune function," says Madelon Peters, Ph.D., professor of psychology in the department of medical, clinical, and experimental psychology at Universiteit Maastricht in the Netherlands.

The way you perceive stress.
Losing a job may be a major stressor for one woman, while another views it as a chance for new opportunity. The brain is in the driver's seat—it determines how much of a change there is in hormonal stress response, which in turn affects any changes in the immune system.

"Perceived stress depends not only on someone's coping resources but also on other moderators, like social support," says Dr. Peters. If you have friends galore supporting you, the effects of your stress will be lowered; but if you have no one to call, stress's effects will be magnified. One study showed that lonely patients had higher cortisol levels and decreased NK cell numbers

WOMEN ASK WHY

Why do more heart attacks occur on Monday than on any other day?

A landmark German study in the mid-1990s showed that Monday morning is the most likely time of the week you'll suffer a heart attack. (In the study, 20 percent more heart attacks took place on Mondays.) And Mondays and the end of the workweek are also the most common times for dangerous heart rhythm disturbances.

The increase in heart attack risk was highest among study participants who were employed outside the home—they experienced fewer than the expected number of heart attacks on Sunday, but on Monday the likelihood that they would be stricken increased to 33 percent more than the expected probability.

One reason that Mondays are so dangerous could be the panic associated with Monday mornings. You wake up with a headache from too much wine and too little sleep, you didn't finish the work you planned to do on Sunday, and you have the whole week looming ahead.

Although it's easy to blame all the stress on work, much of the Monday stress is actually associated with bad time management. Women who don't manage their time well and set priorities can really get themselves into a bind. And that bind tends to squeeze most tightly when the alarm blares early Monday morning.

The Monday heart attack connection could also be due to the stress of a change in routine. The 5-day work schedule forces us to cram all of our relaxing into 2 days, which can make it difficult to switch gears into work mode once Monday rolls around.

Expert consulted
Carolyn Dean, M.D.
Author of Dr. Dean's Complementary Natural Prescriptions for Common Ailments
City Island, New York

compared to patients with social support.

How much control you have over the stress. Studies show that a single session of inescapable electric shock in rats made their tumors grow faster than rats exposed to a shock they could get away from. "And this has been generalized to humans," says Dr. Peters. Although experimental evidence is rather scarce, it's commonly thought that a stressor you can't control, such as a relative with a terminal illness, has a much worse effect on your immune system than one you can control, such as a coworker who wears on your nerves.

Getting Specific

Everyone has a unique immune system," says Marianne Frieri, M.D., Ph.D., associate professor of medicine and pathology at the State University of New York at Stony Brook and director of allergy and immunology at Nassau University Medical Center in East Meadow, New York. It's like each of us is all programmed to suffer from certain conditions when our immune system hits a low point. Some women get migraines, some get gastrointestinal troubles, others get hives.

That said, here are some of the specific manifestations of chronic stress on the immune system.

Stress and allergies. Stress can contribute to allergic reactions, but exactly how is a tricky question. "If stress has an immunosuppressive effect, one would think a stress response might be beneficial for allergies (because allergic flares would be suppressed as well), but it's more com-

REAL-LIFE SCENARIO
Stress May Be Affecting Her Fertility

Jane, 37, is a high-powered consultant who travels 75 percent of the time. She and her husband, Bill, have been trying to get pregnant for a year now. They've had all the tests, and the doctors can find nothing physically wrong with either of them. What should she do?

Research on the relationship between stress and infertility recently took a turn. It used to be that whenever we thought of stress, we thought of anxiety. But there's not a whole lot of compelling evidence linking anxiety and infertility. Instead, there's more evidence linking *clinical depression* with infertility. So for Jane, it's probably not the anxiety of her travel that's contributing to her fertility.

There are a number of other factors (some related to her hectic traveling schedule and some not) that could be contributing to her infertility, however. The first thing to look at is whether or not she's having sex midcycle. If she's gone 75 percent of the time, unless she's arranged her work schedule so she's always home midcycle, she only had 3 total months of trying, which isn't many.

Also, frequent time changes can interfere with the menstrual cycle. So even if Jane makes sure she's home every month on day 14, because of time zone changes, her body could actually be ovulating on day 18 instead, when she's headed out again.

plex than that," says Dr. Peters. "It seems that people with allergies may have an immune system that functions in a different way than most," she says. "For example, a group of children with atopic dermatitis, an allergic skin condition, and a group without the allergy were both asked to speak in public." (Public speaking is one of the few stressors that, in an experimental situation, make cortisol rise). "The healthy children showed increased cortisol levels, but the atopic dermatitis children didn't," says Dr. Peters.

Jane's lifestyle factors also may be affecting her fertility. Many women who travel a lot don't have the greatest health habits. High caffeine consumption can suppress fertility, as can a poor diet, weight loss, or weight gain. Drinking more than one alcoholic beverage per week can hinder fertility. And if Jane is exercising a lot to deal with the stress of travel, that could also make her less likely to conceive.

If Jane has already considered all these factors and adjusted her life to eliminate them, the next step would be to look at her mental history. Does she have a history of depression? Research shows that women with a history of depression are twice as likely to have infertility problems than women without such a history. And is she depressed now? A traveling lifestyle can be overwhelming.

If Jane is not and has never been depressed, she should see a reproductive endocrinologist. In fact, the general recommendation is that if you're over 35 and have been trying unsuccessfully to get pregnant for 6 months, you should see a reproductive endocrinologist, no matter what your mental health history.

Expert consulted
Alice Domar, Ph.D.
Assistant professor of medicine
Harvard Medical School

This difference in the way the immune system reacted to stress may be rooted in the T helper cells. T cells come in two types—Th1 and Th2. Th1 cells control bacterial infection, and Th2 cells turn on the allergic response. "Some women have more Th1 cells, some have more Th2, and some women have high or low levels of both," says Dr. Frieri. When stress suppresses their immune systems, the women with higher levels of Th2 cells are the ones more likely to get an allergic reaction.

Another theory is that the immune system is

like a kettle—it can fill up with only so many immune burdens before it overflows. So if you're under psychological stress and simultaneously fighting an infection, and then you get a huge dose of something you're allergic to (like ragweed), you're going to get an allergy attack. You can empty your immune kettle a bit by steering clear of allergens as best you can. You can also try to stay away from environmental pollutants, such as smoke, heavy metals, fumes, and other toxins that can add burdens to your kettle.

Stress and autoimmune diseases. An autoimmune disease occurs when the immune system attacks the body's own cells, which eventually leads to cell and tissue damage. For example, in the case of multiple sclerosis, the immune system attacks the myelin sheath surrounding some nerve fibers, which results in muscle weakness and vision problems, among other symptoms.

As with allergies, it seems logical that stress would suppress symptoms of autoimmune diseases, but it doesn't—it worsens them. Just as with allergies, researchers suspect a woman with an autoimmune disease may have an immune system that functions differently than that of a woman not prone to autoimmune diseases.

"It's quite clear that stress makes the symptoms of autoimmune diseases, like rheumatoid arthritis or lupus, worse, but it's not clear whether or not stress actually makes the disease itself worse," says Randy Schapiro, M.D., clinical professor of neurology at the University of Minnesota and director at Fairview Multiple Sclerosis Center in Minneapolis.

The science behind the stress and autoimmune disease relationship isn't entirely known, but there are a few theories. One is that stress introduces hormones that slow down the maturation of B cells. This gives the B cells less time to develop, leading to difficulties in recognizing self from nonself cells and, ultimately, to the destruction of specific parts of the body.

Stress and skin diseases. Just as some women get headaches when they're stressed and others run to the bathroom, some women's skin breaks out. Research continues to support the link between stress and the severity of the skin disease eczema, which results in red, itchy, and cracked skin. Emotional stressors don't cause eczema, but they exacerbate it. "It's not so cut-and-dried—that the stress hits today, and then, next week, the eczema flares—but the two do seem to go hand-in-hand for some people," says Marsha Gordon, M.D., associate clinical professor and vice chairperson of the dermatology department at Mount Sinai School of Medicine in New York City.

Acne is another skin condition that may worsen with stress. "If you're acne-prone, it's almost guaranteed that you're going to break out during stressful times, like around your wedding," says Dr. Gordon.

Stress and colds and flu. "It seems that whether or not you get infected with a virus has little to do with stress; however, whether or not the virus makes you sick does," says Dr. Peters. In one study, she says, researchers monitored the stress levels of more than 400 people and then infected them with one of five cold viruses or a placebo.

Those who scored high on stress were more likely to get a cold, even though all participants were infected, Dr. Peters says. So a virus may hitch a ride in your body for a few days, but if you're relatively stress-free and your immune system is strong, your soldiers can keep it at bay.

Stress and healing. Your immune system not only protects you from illness; it also helps heal you when you're sick or injured. Stress can slow down that healing. "Stressors, such as school exams or caring for a sick relative, have been found to slow tissue repair," says Dr. Coe. Scientists measure this by making a small cut on the skin or gums and then watching the rate of healing as the tissue regrows. "And regrowth is markedly impaired during times of stress," he says.

In addition, stress has been shown to slow the rate of blister healing and recovery from surgery. The exact mechanisms behind this phenomenon aren't clear, although one theory suggests that stress may decrease the production of substances that encourage inflammation due to infection and aid in healing, says Dr. Peters.

How much the immune system is suppressed depends on how major and how enduring the stressor is, as well as your emotional capacity to manage it. "School exams may inhibit immunity for a week," says Dr. Coe, "while losing a loved one can cause immune changes for a few months."

Stress and Cancer

You don't *really* know stress until you've been told you have cancer, says Dorothy Leone-Glasser, R.N. And she should know. She's survived three different cancers—melanoma and vaginal and cervical cancer.

"Sure, life is stressful to begin with. But cancer goes beyond stress. It's something that permeates every aspect of your life," says Leone-Glasser, a holistic health counselor in Atlanta and founder of the Coping Program, a program that integrates traditional and holistic concepts of wellness to help people deal with cancer or other serious illness.

Stress is as much a part of cancer as chemotherapy and radiation. There's even some suspicion that stress may have something to do with the formation of cancer, and numerous studies suggest it affects the disease's progression.

Does Stress Cause Cancer?

Scientists know that stress triggers certain reactions in the nervous and endocrine systems that in turn affect immunity by altering the release of antibodies and natural killer cells. But there's no proof that stress weakens the immune system enough to let cancer grab a toehold, says Syed Nasir, M.D., a neuro-oncologist at the Culicchia Neurological Clinic in New Orleans.

In fact, some research *disputes* any link between personal stress and the development of cancer. For example:

- A study of 332 women at the Leeds General Infirmary in England found that those with breast cancer were no more likely to have experienced a major stressful life event than women diagnosed with a benign lump.
- A study of 8,000 healthy women followed for more than 15 years by the University of Peace at the United Nations found that stress factors alone had little effect on whether or not women developed cancer.

The bottom line: If you're blaming your workaholic schedule or bad marriage for your cancer, stop. The only definitive way stress can contribute to cancer is through lifestyle choices, says Dr. Nasir. "Some people who experience a lot of stress start smoking and drinking, which then leaves them more open to developing cancer."

On the Front Lines
An Oncology Social Worker

Hester Hill Schnipper jokes that her phone number must be written on a bathroom stall somewhere. Every day, the chief of oncology social work at Beth Israel Deaconess Medical Center in Boston gets calls from people newly diagnosed with cancer. They're looking for help, comfort, guidance, and just someone to talk to.

And Hill Schnipper is a perfect person to talk to. First off, she's been an oncology social worker for 21 years. During her social work training and first years of employment, she found she especially liked working with cancer patients and their families. When her father, a nonsmoker, died of lung cancer, she became committed to the work in a new way.

Not only that, but her husband is a medical oncologist, so she lives with the disease and its repercussions every day. But perhaps the one thing that makes her the ideal person to turn to is her own diagnosis of breast cancer in 1993. "So I've seen this from both sides of the desk," she says.

Hill Schnipper says the most stressful and overwhelming time for those with cancer is immediately after they've been diagnosed. "You feel that your life is out of control—you're not sleeping, you're not eating, you're crying all the time, you're having panic attacks. I tell them all of this is normal, and that's comforting for them to hear," she says.

She helps them find the right resources to make decisions. She also has a frank discussion about the stress they're going to be under and how they can deal with it. "I'll say, 'These are the six most difficult things that you are going to face.' Then I go through what we can do to eliminate stress in those areas," she says.

It's the people she meets—even under these stressful circumstances—that make her job fulfilling, she says. "I get much more than I give." But she, too, experiences stress—so she often takes her own advice. "I try to treat myself well. I talk about it, and I try to have joy in my life," she says.

Once You Have Cancer

Once a doctor says you have cancer, however, all the uncertainty about stress and cancer dissolves like cotton candy in the rain. As much as the cancer itself, anxiety becomes a constant companion. "What I most often hear is 'I'm scared. I was fine one day and now I'm dealing with a life-threatening illness,'" says Anne Coscarelli, Ph.D., founding director of the Rhonda Flemming Mann Resource Center for Women with Cancer at the Jonsson Cancer Center at the University of California, Los Angeles. "It happens so suddenly for many people."

"The stress and uncertainty of cancer is enough to stop even the most 'together' people in their tracks," says Philadelphia oncologist Marisa Weiss, M.D., author of *Living beyond Breast Cancer, A Survivor's Guide.* "Stress is written all over their faces and really limits their ability to listen, understand, and make decisions on a vast amount of new information that can determine their lives."

Once you move beyond the initial shock, however, the reality of living with cancer hits—and the stress can be even more overpowering than that of the initial diagnosis. The questions come from all sides: What kind of treatment will I choose? Will it make me sick? Will I lose my hair? Who will take care of the kids? Who will take care of me? How do I tell people at work?

But there's more to cancer-related

stress than sleepless nights and constant worrying. While stress may not weaken your immune system to the point of causing cancer, once you're sick, the effects of stress on your immune system could make things worse. The hormone cortisol—which your body produces in response to stress—may stimulate tumor growth. In one study of patients operated on for breast and stomach cancer, those whose cortisol levels did not decrease within 2 weeks of surgery had shorter survival times than those whose levels did decline. Stress also elevates the hormone prolactin, known to help tumors grow.

It's thought that stress affects natural killer cells, which seek out and destroy cancer cells. In one study from Ohio State University, researchers found that women with breast cancer who reported high stress levels actually had fewer natural killer cells and didn't respond as well to gamma interferon—a compound the body produces to enhance killer cell activity.

And, of course, when you're stressed, you don't sleep well, you don't eat right, and you often don't do the very things you need to do to get better. "The better care you take of yourself, both physically and emotionally, the stronger you will feel as you face the many challenges brought about by cancers and their treatments," Dr. Coscarelli says.

Coping with Cancer Stress

If there's any positive news, it's this: Studies show that controlling cancer-related stress not only is doable but can improve your well-being and hasten your recovery. An Ohio State University study of 115 women with Stage II and Stage III breast cancer found that women who underwent a stress reduction program had significantly lower levels of the stress hormone cortisol and 25 percent higher levels of an antibody known to fight breast tumors.

Any stress-reducing exercise—from deep breathing to guided imagery—can help you deal with the cancer anxiety. But as science and the women who have fought these battles themselves can attest, there are some stress-reduction techniques unique to cancer.

Get informed. "As soon as patients connect to information, experts, and each other, develop a plan of action, and know what to expect, their stress is substantially reduced," says Dr. Weiss, who started a Web site, www.breastcancer.org, specifically for this reason.

The Web is filled with information about cancer, but so are libraries, hospital reading rooms, and your own doctor's waiting room. The more you know, the more control over your disease and your life you'll feel you have, says Dr. Weiss.

Join a support group. In people with cancer, social support takes on a new level of importance. Three randomized trials have shown that those with breast cancer, melanoma, and lymphoma lived longer when they had high levels of social support.

Often that support comes from strangers, as women with cancer join support groups of other women with cancer. These groups provide a safe place to talk about worries and fears, typically with a level of honesty that would be impossible to exhibit before well-meaning friends and family.

In support groups, just about everyone knows exactly what you're going through, says Leone-Glasser. "These people understand how you feel from the moment you open your eyes in the morning till you close them at night." You can talk about throwing up after chemo, finding hunks of hair in your brush, and feeling so tired that the simple act of making your bed is enough to unhinge you.

Science bears out the benefits of support groups. In one study, conducted at Stanford

Choosing a Support Group

A cancer support group should be a source of comfort and relief, not another source of stress. But with so many out there, choosing one can be overwhelming. Sandra Kafenbaum, social worker and support group coordinator of the Statewide Breast Cancer Hotline and Support Program at Adelphi University School of Social Work in Garden City, New York, recommends the following:

Call group leaders and feel free to ask questions. It may take more than one meeting to see if the group works for you. If it doesn't meet your needs, leave. Upon leaving, think about asking the group leader for other suggestions.

Decide how often you want to meet. Some groups meet weekly, some twice a month, some once a month. Also decide if you want a group where everyone attends every meeting, or one where you can drop in when you want.

Think about group size. Decide how big or small a group you'll be comfortable with. Some groups are limited in size, while others are open to all.

Ask if the group has a specialty. There are groups for the individual type of cancer, for women who have just been diagnosed, for women whose cancer has spread. Depending on your situation, you can decide just how broad or specific a group you want.

Consider the content. Is it an educational support meeting, where you discuss treatment options and lifestyle questions? Or is it an open forum to express your feelings? Also consider how it's run. Some groups are structured with speakers, while others are open to whoever wants to talk.

University School of Medicine, women with metastatic breast cancer assigned to a support group where they were encouraged to express their feelings survived 18 months longer than those who weren't in any group.

There's another stress-relieving benefit to support groups: hope. "You'll meet other women who have not only survived but thrived," says Linda Burrowes, cofounder of Your Bosom Buddies, a support group in Miami. "You meet people who are longtime survivors. You need to know that there is life after cancer and that it can be a very fulfilling life."

Express yourself honestly. Are you ticked off that you got cancer? Good. Then let it be known. Scream, cry, yell, curse, vent. Expressing your true feelings is key to coping. In breast cancer patients, for example, there's evidence that those who express more "negative" emotions—even anger and uncooperativeness—actually live longer.

A study at the University of Kansas found that women with breast cancer who talked about their fears and emotions had more energy, less distress, and fewer cancer-related medical visits. It's thought that letting it all out discharges stress, anger, and other negative emotions and could positively influence both your hormonal and immune systems.

"The feelings have to come out. You need to work through them, and then the goal is to get to a place where you feel like you can move on," says Sandra Kafenbaum, a social worker and support group coordinator of the Statewide Breast Cancer Hotline and Support Program at Adelphi University School of Social Work in Garden City, New York.

The last thing you want to do is shut down and cloak yourself in denial—what experts call "avoidance." A study at the University of Manitoba in Winnipeg found that women with breast cancer who faced their fears were significantly better adjusted than other women and took a more active role in their treatment decisions.

In addition to participating in a support group, you can write in a journal or just talk. To friends and family, or to anyone who will listen, says Hester Hill Schnipper, chief of oncology social work at Beth Israel Deaconess Medical Center in Boston. Need someone to talk to but don't know where to turn? Call the Adelphi Breast Cancer Hotline at (800) 877-8077. Volunteers can put you in touch with resources in your area of the country.

And when you talk, talk honestly. Be blunt about what you want and need, says Kafenbaum. "Women think we can still do it all—*even* when we have cancer. We've also been taught to be polite, even if we're not getting what we need."

That all goes out the window when you have cancer. Be frank with yourself and others about your capabilities. If someone asks you to do a favor and you don't want to, say no. If you need someone to take care of the kids while you recover, ask. And if an overbearing relative is hurting rather than helping, speak up—and then tell her exactly what would be helpful, Kafenbaum says.

WOMAN TO WOMAN
Breast Cancer Made Her Stronger

In 1988, Carol Rogers was diagnosed with Stage II breast cancer. She wanted to learn more about breast cancer and talk to other women like herself but found there was nowhere for her to turn in her hometown of Evansville, Indiana. So she got together with four other women with breast cancer—and the Woman to Woman support group was born. More than 12 years later, Rogers still gives and receives support from this amazing group of women. This is her story.

When I was diagnosed, we didn't have anything like a support group in our community. So when the five of us met over lunch, we decided to invite anyone we knew with breast cancer to our group. When we had our first Woman to Woman meeting, 22 women showed up. Some of us have been to almost every meeting since 1989.

We keep it simple. We're not affiliated with any organization. We meet at our local library once a month. Some meetings include guest speakers; all include a time for sharing. We never have refreshments, so no one has to do any work. There are no membership lists or dues, no mailing list, no committee sign-up sheets. We never give out the list of names of members to anyone. We just share stories and the latest research, and we talk about our fears and laughter and joy.

That's what our group is about: women connecting with other women. Being diagnosed with breast cancer is like becoming a member of a sorority you didn't ask to join. We became part of a sisterhood. And we want the support of other women who are going through it.

But don't get the wrong impression—it's not a pity party. It's amazing how much humor you'll find. The women tell stories that are really funny that we can all relate to. Sure, there are sad moments, but overall it's a wonderful, upbeat group.

And I've found that each individual comes for different reasons. Some want reassurance, some want information, some want to vent frustrations and fears, some want to help and encourage others.

Now several of us come to support the newly diagnosed—it shows them that support doesn't stop even when the cancer is gone.

Find meaning in your illness. When Burrowes was diagnosed with breast cancer in 1997, she didn't see it as a tragedy. In fact, she saw a need—and an opportunity.

Following reconstructive surgery after her mastectomy for breast cancer, she wanted to talk to other women who had undergone the procedure, and looked for a group that provided such support. She couldn't find any. So she started her own group, Your Bosom Buddies.

Even though she's been cancer-free for 3 years, she still devotes most of her time to other women with breast cancer. "It is my way of coping. It's not that I am happy that I got breast cancer, but my life has been so enriched because of it. The people I have met will be my friends for the rest of my life," Burrowes says.

It's a theme you hear from many women with cancer: "I wouldn't have chosen this road, but I have been enriched and changed by the experience," Dr. Coscarelli says many of her patients tell her.

Some experts believe that finding meaning in your cancer improves your psychological state, which enables you to better handle the illness and its concurrent stress. Those who use it as a catalyst for change find they often come out of it a more enriched—and less stressed—person.

Many women find that their cancer awakens a need to help other people. They start to volunteer with various organizations or help other women with cancer. For others, it's a call to do what they've always wanted—travel, go back to school, begin to paint. "Basically, they're nurturing themselves. And that has an impact on their emotional and physical well-being," Kafenbaum says.

For Leone-Glasser, her cancer diagnosis awakened her to her real purpose in life, which is what led her to create the Coping Program. "Part of your wellness comes from helping someone else," she says.

PART THREE

The Nine Circles of a Woman's Stress

The First Circle: Commuting

Diane Nahl's father had always been an aggressive driver. So aggressive that when Nahl, now a Ph.D. and information scientist at the University of Hawaii at Manoa, turned 16, she didn't even want to get her own driver's license.

Although she finally obtained it, her behavior behind the wheel was nothing like her father's. "I'm overly cautious, accommodating," she says.

So when she rode with her husband, Leon James, Ph.D., a professor of psychology at the University of Hawaii at Honolulu, she held on for dear life.

Recalls Dr. James: "I was rushing, competing, opportunistic—switching lanes, taking risks. People who were my passengers had to put up with everything. . . . If they were scared or knocked about, they just had to adjust. Finally, Diane told me: 'Leon, you'd better change the way you're driving.'"

So the couple began looking not only at his behavior but at that of other drivers, too. They surveyed hundreds of university students and visitors to their Web site www.DrDriving.org and researched the habits of drivers dating back

to the Roman chariots. (Yes, the ancients, too, had road rage.)

"The thing about aggressive drivers is that no one thinks *they* are one," Dr. James says. "But we all are."

Aggressive driving causes about 28,000 deaths a year on U.S. roads. "Two-thirds of fatalities on the road are due to aggressive driving," says Arnold P. Nerenberg, Ph.D., a psychologist in Whittier, California, who has researched the subject.

It's so pervasive that many Americans view it as an epidemic. In a survey by the AAA Foundation for Traffic Safety in Washington, D.C., 35 percent of respondents said aggressive drivers are the most serious problem on our roads, compared with distracted drivers (31 percent); drunk drivers (29 percent); and others (5 percent).

Aggressive driving is not only a serious, growing problem, it's also a behavior that we learn as children when we take car trips with Mom, Dad, Grandma, or even the babysitter, say Dr. James and Dr. Nahl, coauthors of *Road*

Rage and Aggressive Driving: Steering Clear of Highway Warfare.

The good news is that we can learn to change our behavior. To enjoy a more peaceful commute. To make our highways, ourselves, and our families safer.

The Madness Begins

Remember that driver you tailed last time you were late for a meeting? Or that parking space you scooped up at the mall just as another car was turning toward it?

No, you're not a bad person. "Within the human psyche is an urge to release our aggression on anonymous others when we feel justified," says Dr. Nerenberg. Think soldiers in combat.

As in warfare, anonymity is a major reason for aggressive driving. We see cars—inanimate boxes of metal—not real people on our roads, especially in urban areas. "It's not a human like ourselves, with frustrations and loves and insecurities and aspirations," Dr. Nerenberg says.

Other common reasons we may drive aggressively: We're hurrying and someone slows us down. Another driver breaks the rules, such as switching lanes without signaling. Someone looks at us "the wrong way"; or she steals *our* parking space.

Add a growing number of cars on roads ill-designed to carry them, and you've got the perfect mix for what Dr. Nahl and Dr. James call a culture tantrum.

STEERING CLEAR OF AGGRESSIVE DRIVERS

Hazardous driving arrived not with the Ford or the Chrysler but with public roads, says Diane Nahl, Ph.D., an information scientist at the University of Hawaii at Manoa and coauthor of *Road Rage and Aggressive Driving: Steering Clear of Highway Warfare.*

The British called it "furious driving," says Dr. Nahl. In England, as early as the 1800s, towns passed laws against citizens' driving their horses home after drinking at the saloon.

Here are some modern-day tips from the AAA Foundation for Traffic Safety and other driving experts. To avoid angry drivers:

Don't cut off other drivers. Use your turn signal to show your intentions, and make sure you have plenty of room to make your move.

Don't drive slowly in the left lane. In many states, the left lane is reserved for passing. Even if you are driving the speed limit, move to the right and let others pass— if only to avoid inciting the drivers and endangering yourself.

Never follow too closely. Tailgating is an almost certain way to spark a driver's wrath. Leave about a 2-second space between your car and the one in front of you. (When the car ahead of you passes a fixed point, such as a speed limit sign, you should be able to count "one, one thousand, two, one thousand" before passing the same point.)

Keep your hands on the wheel. Never make obscene or angry gestures, such as shaking your head or fist in disgust. Don't flash your headlights or blow your horn out of anger. Avoid eye contact.

Recognizing the Problem

Although "aggressive driving" and "road rage" are often used interchangeably, they are different.

Road rage is the deliberate, criminal intent to injure or kill a motorist or pedestrian, say, by firing a gun or running them off the road. Aggressive driving is more spontaneous—and carried out by a typically calm individual, like ourselves. Dr. James defines it as "imposing your own level of risk on others." Tailgating is one example. Even the type of vehicle you drive may affect your attitude. Women are most daring in sport utility vehicles, light trucks, and family and luxury cars, while men exhibit bravado in light trucks and sports cars.

We're also most likely to let loose during peak travel times (think Friday afternoons), during the summer, and under moderately congested conditions.

Some clues that you've become an aggressive driver:

- Feeling more stress while driving
- Feeling enraged, competitive, or compelled to drive dangerously
- Acting hostile, cursing more often, yelling or honking at other drivers, or making insulting gestures
- Speeding, tailgating, or cutting off others

WOMAN TO WOMAN
She Learned to Control Her Road Rage

Lynn, a graphics designer from Orwigsburg, Pennsylvania, has spent the last 9 years commuting to her office, about 40 miles away. She rarely minded the drive. But when the inevitable road construction project, traffic accident, or inconsiderate driver obstructed her smooth commute, Lynn became enraged—and wasn't shy about showing it. Then, about 7 years ago, something caused her to suddenly change her driving habits. This is her story.

My 45- to 50-minute interstate commute normally was peaceful. But my drive sometimes stretched by as much as 2 to 4 hours if an accident occurred ahead. Often a road construction project might delay my drive by 20 minutes or more.

My workdays were already long—sometimes 10 hours a day Monday through Friday, plus an occasional Saturday. My lone drive gave me plenty of time to think about problems at work or elsewhere. Getting stuck on the highway simply added to my stress.

So, whenever a driver tailgated me, cut me off without signaling, or even looked at me the wrong way, something inside me just snapped. I saw nothing but red. I'd get angry and tailgate them—screaming, flashing my headlights, using obscene gestures. Sometimes, enraged, I'd race another driver down the highway at 90 miles an hour.

I just got so worked up; my heart raced long after the

"Braking" Old Habits

Change means first acknowledging that you drive aggressively, Dr. James says. Then you must "witness it." Lay a tape recorder on the car seat beside you and talk about your feelings as you drive. Do this daily for a week or so. Later, listen to the tape. "Everybody is shocked at who they really are behind the wheel," he says.

Or carry a notepad and pen, and after you park, write down everything you thought and

felt during your drive. Ask: "What made me angry?" "How long did I feel that way?" You'll see a trend that can be revealing.

Then address the problem.

Tackle one habit at a time. For example, if you typically follow too closely, practice keeping at least one car length between you and the next car. Once it becomes automatic (experts tell us it takes 21 days for a new habit to become ingrained), begin to change another behavior.

Be a supportive driver. "Think about posother driver disappeared. And there I was, with nothing but all this negative emotion.

My friends and coworkers could hardly believe this generally congenial person became such a madwoman on the highway! I even surprised myself. After each incident, I would think, "That was pretty stupid. What did I gain from that?"

Then, while driving about 7 years ago, I saw a car literally fly off the road and flip over. Although the accident wasn't caused by aggression—the driver had apparently fallen asleep at the wheel—I was so shaken, I had to pull off the highway.

"That could have been me," I thought. I needed to calm down behind the wheel, to let things go. I talked to a counselor, who helped me make some positive changes in my routine and my attitude.

Now I carry a couple of books and some magazines in the backseat. If traffic stops, I turn off my engine, relax, and read. I also carry a cellular phone; I call my office if I think I'll be late.

When I see other people driving too fast, too slowly, or inappropriately, I tell myself that reacting angrily could cost me my life. I don't let it grab hold of me. I even make room for drivers if they're merging onto the highway. If someone's tailgating, I'll try to move to the right and get out of the way.

Sometimes, when I'm stuck in traffic, I look in my rearview mirror at the person behind me who's fretting and steaming. Then, I take a deep, relaxing breath, reach for a magazine, and enjoy those few moments I have to myself.

vertently cut someone off, make an apologetic gesture they can see. Just be certain that your motion is be seen as friendly and not confrontational. Some drivers blow kisses, and in an American Automobile Association survey, one said she carries a white flag attached to a towel so she can wave it. One woman said she felt so bad once when she cut someone off that her children, who also were in the car, pulled crayons and paper from their backpacks, drew rainbows, and held them up to the driver behind them. He responded with a grin.

Breathe deeply. If you get stuck in a traffic jam, practice deep, relaxing belly breathing, says Angela Stroup, R.N., a certified hypnotherapist and assistant professor at Eastern Virginia Medical School in Norfolk, Virginia. Let your belly inflate like a balloon as you slowly inhale to the count of four. Let it deflate, as you exhale and count to eight. Doing this several times helps reduce the muscle tension, racing heart, and high blood pressure that may accompany anger or stress.

Seek professional help. If you simply can't lay aside your anger behind the wheel, consider talking to a counselor. Remember, you could be legally responsible or, at the least, embarrassed—for an action taken in a moment of rage.

itive alternatives as to why somebody did something that looks stupid to you," Dr. James says. Maybe the other driver just received bad news, doesn't feel well, or is new to the area.

Learn to accommodate. If someone scoots in ahead of you, give her some room, instead of racing to close the gap. "You'll discover that you like being a supportive driver, and it's less stressful," Dr. James says. It's also contagious. If we're courteous to others, they're more likely to pass it on.

Acknowledge your mistakes. If you inad-

For instance, Dr. Nerenberg had one patient, a normally calm woman, who screamed at another driver on the highway. That evening the woman met the driver at a dinner party. Turns out the driver she'd verbally abused was the wife of her husband's boss. Talk about being embarrassed!

The Second Circle: Illness

What's that saying—all the money in the world can't buy good health?

So how, then, do you cope when you or someone you love gets sick?

Whether it's a parent, spouse, child, or even ourselves, an illness brings with it an entirely new level of stress. And since women are typically the caregivers when someone falls ill (including ourselves), our stress increases not only in intensity but also in frequency.

The key to surviving this kind of stress (and not getting sick or sicker yourself) is to break it down into manageable bits and tackle one area at a time. Here's how.

Enduring the Emotional Toll

The emotional strain caused by a serious illness—either your own or that of a loved one—is different from the everyday, ordinary stress of traffic jams, burned dinners, and grumpy bosses, says Stephen M. Tovian, Ph.D., director of health psychology at Evanston Northwestern Health Care in Evanston, Illinois. "The stakes are much higher when you're dealing with life-and-death situations," says Dr. Tovian.

That's because the stress hits in so many areas.

Fear. Initially, most patients fear three things: death, incapacitation, and, most of all, pain. "In fact, once they've resigned themselves to a terminal illness, people often say that they're not afraid to die—they just don't want to suffer," says Dr. Tovian. These fears are very common, and they're usually the first emotions a disease causes.

Changing roles. If you're used to being the family nurturer, you'll have to adjust to being cared for during your illness. In the same way, your mother's illness may put you into the role of the mother and her into the role of the child. These changes alter the dynamic of important relationships and create strain.

Loss of control. "You're at the mercy of the illness, the doctors, the insurance companies, the people caring for you," Dr. Tovian says.

Exposure to the unknown. Throughout the course of an illness, you'll have to deal with unfamiliar people, places, and even words as you

COPING WHEN A LOVED ONE DIES

Unlike many stressful life events, loss—especially the death of a loved one—is not optional. "It is part of the texture of human life," says Robert Neimeyer, Ph.D., professor of psychology and a grief specialist at the University of Memphis in Tennessee.

At midlife, we are statistically at greater risk for losing a parent. But we may lose a husband, child, or long-time friend. Their deaths may occur across our lives or in clusters.

Feelings of grief—denial, depression—are natural in the aftermath. They may be especially intense or prolonged if the death was unexpected or unnatural, as with a suicide, a homicide, an accident, or the loss of a child. Only with time will our pain pass as we move into acceptance, says Dr. Neimeyer.

But acceptance doesn't mean we must forget our loved one, despite society's expectation that we "get over it and get along." "Our culture has perpetuated a number of very mischievous and destructive fictions about what grief and loss consist of," Dr. Neimeyer says.

It emphasizes the importance of letting go, saying goodbye, seeking closure. "I think the goal of grieving is not saying 'goodbye'; it's learning how to say 'hello' again, to find a symbolic reconnection with the one who has died," he says.

He suggests that we celebrate our loved one. In our initial grief—at the viewing, perhaps—set up a memory table of photos and personal mementos, such as trophies or crafts, that illustrate the person's life.

Welcome visitors to your home to share tears, hugs, and memories. Consider playing the person's favorite music, reading aloud poems or Bible verses he or she enjoyed.

"The way in which we integrate these losses into our own lives is profoundly important in determining the people we become," Dr. Neimeyer says.

In time, often over years, our trauma can evolve into personal growth, changing us in ways we never anticipated.

"Becoming more empathetic to the pain of others is a common outcome," Dr. Neimeyer says.

We may also experience a renewal of life or a focus on living more consciously, or provide greater attention to our relationships. We may feel wiser, less constrained.

For instance, a retired secretary whose husband died suddenly of a heart attack later joined a volunteer program that provided mentoring for troubled teens. After her training period, she spent 9 months away from home, teaching and counseling. She turned her grief into personal growth.

"There is so much possibility of good things coming from these bad things," Dr. Neimeyer says. "While loss is not to be welcomed, it is to be recognized and used well."

struggle to decode the medical jargon flying at you. These changes can be stressful enough under normal circumstances, but they're even more so when your health is at stake.

Social stigma. Many people fear that an illness marks them as somehow weak or inferior, Dr. Tovian says. "Our culture values independence and health, and some people mourn the loss of being seen that way."

There are numerous ways, however, to overcome these emotional stresses. They include the following strategies.

Become an expert. In dealing with an illness, knowledge truly is power. "I scoured the Internet and a nearby university library to find out everything I could about my diseases," says Carol Sims, a licensed clinical mental health counselor and Episcopal priest from Lewistown, Montana, who has survived three bouts of cancer and a blood platelet disorder.

She kept a notebook and wrote down everything her doctors said. Becoming familiar with the treatments, statistics, and jargon helped her make more informed choices, she said.

"Instead of just telling the doctor to do whatever he thought best, I was able to have intelligent conversations with him about my options," Sims said.

Start in your doctor's office—she may be able to give you educational materials or recommend some good books on the subject.

Find a support group. Groups exist for patients, family members, and caregivers. Chances are there's one in your area—or hit the Internet for e-mail lists and chat rooms. Support groups have been so successful because they provide another shoulder to lean on, one outside your family and friends, says Dr. Tovian. "The members know what you're going through, and they're more than willing to share their wisdom, both emotional and practical," he says.

Define long-term goals. Every illness has a desired end. For some, such as cancer, the goal might be survival. For others, such as a stroke, the goal might be rehabilitation. With a terminal illnesses, the goal might simply be to die with dignity and find meaning in it, says

WOMAN TO WOMAN
She Became Her Mother's Caregiver

When Vicki Gardner's mother was diagnosed with Alzheimer's disease in 1995, the 50-year-old retired recruiter from Fremont, California, was devastated. But she learned how to cope. Here is her story.

When I learned about the diagnosis, I sat in the doctor's office and went completely numb. "Anything but this," I thought. A disease of the mind is the most terrifying kind, because you have no control, no timetable.

My first response was to go to the Internet and find out everything I could. But I soon realized there were things I didn't want to know, like the deterioration and the heartache.

I debated putting her in a nursing home, but since I was divorced with no children, it made sense to keep my mother at home. But it's a solution that every caregiver has to reach individually. It all depends on your life situation and how much time and energy you have to devote to the care of your loved one.

It hasn't been easy caring for my mother. The first time she didn't recognize me, I was heartbroken. She had no clue who I was and kept asking, "Why are you calling me Mom?"

Alzheimer's forces you to go through the grief process even while the patient is still alive. I went through denial, anger, resentment, sadness, and now I've finally learned to accept the disease. I've learned to separate my mother from her disease. She has good days and bad days, and the good days make the bad days worthwhile.

It took me a long time to get to this point. I first turned to prayer, which definitely helped. Then I went online to get

Dr. Tovian. Once you've clearly established what the goals are, sit down with your doctor and draw up a long-term plan to meet them. Chances are you won't follow the plan exactly, but just having one increases your sense of control.

answers to my questions. The doctors I dealt with couldn't answer them, but the people dealing with Alzheimer's can. Online I found answers, but more important, I found *support.* People just like me, trying to understand this disease and trying to keep their loved ones out of nursing homes. The problem with dementia (aside from the obvious) is that every day brought on a new behavior that I had no idea how to handle. I also called the Alzheimer's Association and received recommendations for wonderful books on how to handle my mother's behavior.

It's so important to treat a person with Alzheimer's with kindness and love. If you're tense or angry, she will be, too. So I learned to speak to my mother in a calm, loving voice and then to go into another room and cry or call a friend.

I also learned to cling to the part of her that still remains. If my mother wants to go back in time to 1940, I let her. I used to try to bring her back to reality, but it just confused and upset her. I'll pretend to reminisce about the good old days, even though I have no idea what she's talking about. But it makes her happy, which makes me happy.

At first, I thought I couldn't possibly cope with this disease. But I learned to cope, and it has gotten easier. No matter what, she's still my mother, and I still love her.

Some resources that I found helpful include the book *The 36-Hour Day: A Family Guide to Caring for Persons with Alzheimer's Disease, Related Dementing Illnesses, and Memory Loss in Later Life* by Nancy L. Mace and Peter V. Rabins, M.D.; the Web site www.caregiving.com; local Alzheimer's support groups; and an Alzheimer's e-mail list service (go to www.biostat.wustl.edu/ALZHEIMER/subscribe.html to subscribe)

Define short-term goals. Unfortunately, that long-term plan won't help you get through the day-to-day business of dealing with an illness. You need to focus on the small things, says Susan Folkman, Ph.D., professor of medicine at the University of California, San Francisco.

Even a simple to-do list for each day gives you a sense of purpose, and every task you cross off provides a feeling of accomplishment.

Reassign jobs. An illness often requires a reorganization of who does what, especially if you're the family caregiver and can no longer fulfill your role. So sit down with everyone in the household and make a list of what needs to be done, suggests Susan Heitler, Ph.D., clinical psychologist at the University of Denver School of Professional Psychology and author of *The Power of Two: Secrets to a Strong and Loving Marriage.* Decide what tasks (if any) you can still handle, then let everyone else divvy up the rest of the list.

Recruit supporters. Each of your friends and relatives can help in different ways. One makes you laugh, another has a terrific shoulder to cry on, a third makes the world's best homemade soup. Keep a mental (or actual) list of what their special talents are, and call on them as needed.

Revisit religion. When an illness occurs, a common first reaction is to blame God or to feel spiritually isolated. But a spiritual perspective helps many patients and their families. "The idea of trusting God to help you make the most of your difficult situation can be very comforting," says Dr. Heitler.

Savor positive moments. Every so often, something good comes along to brighten your illness-centered day. It might be a beautiful sunset, a shared laugh, or an acknowledgment of thanks from your loved one. Do everything you can to hold on to this moment, says Dr.

Although every day may not resemble the controlled chaos of the television show ER, working in the emergency room of any hospital is stressful, particularly if the hospital is based in a large, metropolitan area. "It's rushed, it's chaotic, and patients are coming to you for help," says Julie Jatico, R.N., director of emergency services at Centinela Hospital in Inglewood, California. "It's not easy to see people hurt, bleeding, and in pain. As nurses, though, we do learn to deal with it, probably in ways that would offend the general public."

Some of their coping skills include making light of the injuries among themselves. "We don't want to face the fact that the person lying in front of us might die," she says. "To families, this attitude often comes across the wrong way. When they bring in a loved one with an injury, it's the most serious thing in the world. We understand that. But if we had the same emotional involvement that they do, we'd never make it through a shift."

Jatico also tries to view a patient not as a person but as a body. As a problem that needs to be solved. She needs this detachment in order to do her job better. "If I know the person, there's no way I can be calm and help him or her," she says. "I used to work at a trauma center near my parents' home, and eventually I had to find a job somewhere else. Every time a trauma was called in and I'd hear a description that vaguely resembled one of my relatives, I was a wreck."

Still, there are always cases that get to her. "When that happens, we generally talk about them here at work, with other nurses and staff members," she says. "It's difficult to discuss cases with family members who didn't share our experience. I think the strong family bond among the nurses is what helps us handle our emotions."

The Stress of Health

If you've been a caregiver and your patient is now improving, don't think the stress ends. One of the hardest adjustments comes when the person who was sick gets better, says Dr. Heitler.

During the course of an illness, everyone pulls together and helps out. There's an adrenaline surge that keeps you going through the toughest times, and when the crisis is over, you may feel a sudden drop in energy. You may also be vulnerable to colds or other illnesses, since your immune system was compromised by the stress.

Any change, even positive change, is stressful. And just as your various roles may have changed at the beginning of the illness, they'll evolve again when the illness is over. "When handling an illness, a woman may become a superwoman—breadwinner, caregiver, wife, mother," says Dr. Heitler. "Of course she wants the patient to get better and return to a normal life. But on some level she may fear giving up part of her Superwoman identity."

Dr. Heitler recommends consciously addressing the return to your pre-illness life. If you've been handling everything during the illness, redistribute tasks to other family members, including the person who was sick. Once you have fewer tasks on your plate, be glad for the extra time you have. Chances are, you'll soon be grateful that you don't have to be Superwoman anymore.

Folkman. Write it down, tell a friend, take a picture if you have to. The memories of these good moments can sustain you when times get rough.

The Third Circle: Perfectionism and Expectations

I'm a recovering perfectionist," says 45-year-old Cammy with a chuckle and a half smile.

She's not joking, though. This wife and mother, who bakes specialty cakes at her Virginia home, once held such high expectations for herself that she literally smashed any cake that didn't turn out "perfectly."

"If I thought the cake was overbaked by even 1 minute, I would take it outside, feed it to the birds, and bake a new one," says Cammy, who asked that her real name not be used.

"I have some very well-fed wildlife," she says. "But they're not as well-fed as they used to be."

Cammy, like many other perfectionists, finally realized that her exhaustive efforts were self-defeating, based not on the enjoyment of attaining a goal but on a drive to boost her self-worth.

Like Cammy, perfectionists are constantly frustrated and stressed by their own unreasonable self-expectations. Many suffer from anxiety, stomachaches, irritable bowel syndrome, high blood pressure, or hopelessness when they fail to meet their self-imposed standards. Perfectionism may lead to eating disorders—such as anorexia nervosa—major depression, and even suicide.

Perfection, after all, is subjective—unattainable, says Dennis Vidoni, Ph.D., a psychologist and assistant director of counseling at the University of Illinois at Urbana-Champaign.

But like Cammy, we can beat perfectionism while still meeting our goals.

Recognizing Perfectionism

The healthy achiever, says Dr. Vidoni, focuses on the process, not on the outcome or its reflection on her value. She may not do as well as she hoped, but she is able to say: "That's the way it goes. I did the best I could."

The perfectionist, however, sets "excessively high" goals and turns the results into a self-evaluation. "These are goals that, even if you reach them, never satisfy you," he says. "It's more an assessment of yourself: 'Something is wrong with me. I'm impaired, flawed.'"

Perfectionists often fear failure, humiliation, making mistakes, or the disapproval of others. They may work at a turtle's pace to get everything just so, or procrastinate to avoid discomfort—which only prolongs it.

WOMEN ASK WHY

Why am I always so stressed during the holidays?

The desire to do it all is a top reason we stress out at the most festive times. We may try to mail handwritten Christmas cards, trim the tree, decorate the house, bake cookies, give a party, attend parties, see our children's school productions, and buy the perfect gifts.

From November through early January, perfectionism and the stress it causes lead more patients to my door than anything else.

Typically, people become increasingly anxious or increasingly depressed during the holidays. Symptoms include difficulty sleeping, headaches, backaches, ulcers, and tension. You may have less energy or trouble getting motivated, drink more, smoke more, and eat more or less.

Often, patients' symptoms arise from a longing for the perfect, Norman Rockwell kind of holiday.

No matter the cause of your stress, though, you *can* ease your way through the holidays and even experience a little warmth, peace, and joy.

First, remember to focus on the meaning of the holiday. Thanksgiving, after all, is for giving thanks. Christmas, Hanukkah, and Kwanzaa are important religious or cultural holidays, times to share with family and friends. New Year's is for new beginnings.

If you're a perfectionist, list everything you want to do and trim it by one-third. Try baking in February instead of December, and give the homemade gifts when no one expects them. Sign and address holiday cards in July.

In the weeks before the holidays, save time for family when you're not doing anything and you're just hanging out. Most of all, take care of your spiritual side and enjoy.

Expert consulted
Theresa Farrow, M.D.
Psychiatrist and associate clinical professor
University of Oklahoma
Tulsa

"I'm often afraid to start a job because I'm not sure I can do it perfectly," says Cammy.

Perfectionists typically share several false assumptions about themselves and others. These include the following:

- Oversimplification, or black-and-white thinking. This is when you think there are only two paths—the right one and the wrong one. By failing to see shades of gray, you give yourself only two options: success or failure. Talk about stress!
- Overmagnification of problems.
- Minimization of abilities
- Negative predictions about the outcome of your work.
- Assuming that others think the worst of you. For instance, Cammy often feared her reputation would be ruined if a client saw an imperfection in just one of her cakes.

The Roots of Perfectionism

Some research suggests that the perfectionist's personality may be genetic, or inherited. But the perfectionist also can thank—or blame—society and her family for helping her set unrealistic self-expectations.

Our world often rewards perfection. The flawless beauty. The impeccable performance. The best actress.

Parents also convey their expectations of us. The messages may be overt—that a B on our report card should have been an A. Or subtle—maybe it seemed as if your baby sister garnered all the attention at home.

We learn, "if I don't do this, I won't be valued as a person," Dr. Vidoni says. And the messages can stay with us for a lifetime.

Cammy remembers shredding grade-school projects she didn't think would meet her father's unspoken expectations. "I didn't want my dad to see that I couldn't do something as perfectly as he could," she says.

Her younger brother, who shared Dad's penchant for tennis, and her older sister, who consistently achieved A's, seemed perfect in their father's eyes. "I believed if I could be the perfect little girl, then he would love me," Cammy says.

A chubby child, Cammy struggled with anorexia in junior high school. One summer, she ate only apples, cantaloupe, and diet gelatin and went from a size 12 to a 7. This reflected another misconception commonly held by perfectionists, says Dr. Vidoni: "an illusion of control over things. They try to be perfect to gain some control."

Learning That It's Okay to Be Okay

After graduating from college, Cammy overcame her eating disorder and her battle with the scale on her own when she realized that

LIVING WITH PERFECTIONISTS

Do you ask too much from others?

Perfectionists are often inwardly focused, setting excessively high standards for themselves. Not surprisingly, perhaps, many also expect flawless performances from others.

Some points to consider: Are you continually disappointed when others don't meet your expectations? Do you think others are lazy, don't care, or don't take pride in their work? Do you often think you'd perform a task better yourself? Do you frequently clean up others' work?

Then consider yourself an outwardly focused perfectionist, writes Monica Ramirez Basco, Ph.D., in her book *Never Good Enough: How to Use Perfectionism to Your Advantage without Letting It Ruin Your Life.* Since we seldom talk aloud about our standards of performance, it's easy to assume that everyone thinks and works alike.

But these actions can cause problems at home and work, alienating you from peers and family. Here's how to rein in your perfectionistic expectations of others.

⬧ When a coworker or spouse doesn't meet your expectations, be honest. Respectfully tell them what you would rather see or do, and be specific. Tackle one problem at a time. And listen.

⬧ With children, express confidence even when their behavior or schoolwork disappoints you. Praise children based on their work, not their value. Don't reserve compliments and affection for times of achievement. Deliver negative feedback privately and with encouragement.

And if you're not the perfectionist but live with one?

"Be aware of your feelings," says Dennis Vidoni, Ph.D., assistant director of counseling at the University of Illinois at Urbana-Champaign. "And be as honest as you possibly can be, given the situation you are in."

On the job, take directions as suggestions, not demands, Dr. Basco advises in her book. Be calm. If you prefer to carry out a task differently, express confidence, which is more likely to earn you respect. If your productivity, health, or morale is diminished, however, "you can speak to a boss in those terms," Dr. Vidoni says. "The boss may understand that."

her self-expectations were ruining her life. In later years, she talked with a counselor, who helped her see that her perfectionism was a waste of time and energy—not to mention sugar, eggs, butter, and flour!

Gradually, Cammy started to challenge her fears and self-imposed standards, such as worrying about what others thought of her work.

Overcoming perfectionism begins with becoming aware of your misconceptions and understanding where they came from, says Dr. Vidoni, and then challenging them. Talking to a therapist may be helpful, but you can take many steps yourself.

Relinquish control. Ask *less* of yourself. Susan Thomas, who has a master's degree in education and is director of counseling at the State University of New York at Potsdam, challenges stressed, perfectionist students by saying: "Do not study for this test." They're terrified, she says, "but they get the A," because they've already overstudied.

At work, complete a report at 80 percent of your usual effort, says Dr. Vidoni. Learn that others don't see your "imperfection"; only you do. Cammy, for instance, now bakes wedding cakes in 1½ days, instead of 3. No one's complaining, including her family.

Set goals based on your wants and needs. "Everything is a priority for perfectionist women," Thomas says. Be honest; choose what's most important to you and put your energies there.

Look at your vocabulary. Discard either/or thinking and words such as "never," "always," "completely," "totally." Such superlatives leave little room for error.

Say "no." Women often are socialized to be the perfect mother or spouse, says Daniel E. Williams, Ph.D., a clinical psychologist in East Orange, New Jersey. We may try to please everyone but ourselves. When we set boundaries, we gain time *and* the respect of others.

Listen. Listen to your anxieties or feelings of depression, and learn from them. Ask, "What do I fear?" "Have I set myself up for unattainable expectations?" says Dr. Vidoni.

Break down tasks. Perfectionists often are overwhelmed by their monumental agendas. "Focus on the process," says Dr. Vidoni. "Enjoy and learn." For example, if you're beginning a new job, appreciate the challenges each day brings, instead of looking ahead only to the time when you'll be completely familiar, or expert, at what you do.

Be vigilant. Perfectionism often surfaces when you're stressed. Remind yourself that nothing is perfect and that it's okay—even healthy—to cut back, Dr. Vidoni says.

Cammy has taken much of this advice to heart. "I'm learning," she says. "I'm much more relaxed. I have a lot more fun with baking now." She knows that an imperfect cake (whose imperfections are probably visible only to her) won't mar a couple's wedding day. These days, Cammy merely turns the "boo-boo" to the back.

The Fourth Circle: Body Image

No matter where I go or what I put on, there's always this big butt to deal with.
—*Social worker, age 24*

When we were little girls, we played with Barbie. We brushed her hair, dressed her in hot pants, and put her on her little plastic scale that read "110." If Barbie were a person, she'd measure in at 39-18-33—proportions not humanly possible (unless she were to topple over every time she stood up). Yet this was our goal, our ideal. Multiply Barbie by hundreds of heroin-chic, size-2 actresses and models gracing TV and movie screens and magazines, and it's no wonder we're so stressed out about body image.

The key to finding natural calm in this instance is to look beyond the perpetrators of poor body image and learn to appreciate our own unique beauty and worth.

Perpetrator #1: History

It's a memorable scene in *Gone with the Wind*: Scarlett O'Hara wraps her arms around her bedpost and holds on for dear life as Mammy yanks on the corset laces to make her waist ever tinier. "No wonder women weren't productive in society back then—they were too busy fainting," says Edie Raether, a licensed psychotherapist residing in Raleigh, North Carolina. "I mean, talk about stress!"

Then came the Victorian age, when women stayed home to conserve their energy—in an off-the shoulder, hoop-skirted "day dress" made from yards of heavy fabric.

The 1920s brought a radical change from the prudish, feminine Victorian style. "Flappers," as they were called, were the first waifs. The look was boyish. Women cut their hair short and wore sacklike, straight dresses. In contrast to the padded bosoms and hips of Victorian dresses, the goal in that decade was to have as small a bust and hips as possible.

The 1950s brought the fixation back to breasts, and Marilyn Monroe and Jayne Mansfield represented the ideal. Then, in the 1960s, seemingly out of nowhere, an exaggerated version of the flapper reappeared as gaunt Twiggy.

"The designers of that era were primarily men, and I think the stick look was reintroduced

BODY IMAGE IN MEN

It's been well-documented that women's bodies are examined, evaluated, and sexualized more often than men's. "There are older male movie stars who are overweight or bald or have wrinkles, and we accept that in men," says Diana Zuckerman, Ph.D., executive director of the National Center for Policy Research for Women and Families in Washington, D.C. Men don't put as much pressure on themselves as women do to look good. They don't check out their fat thighs in the dressing room for 20 minutes, and they don't refuse ice cream after a shopping trip just because they couldn't fit into a pair of size-10 jeans, she says. Men also claim to feel thin at 105 percent of their ideal body weight, while women don't claim to feel thin until they drop to 90 percent.

Granted, men do feel *some* pressure from society concerning their appearance, but the standards are more flexible. "A man may worry a little about his hairline, but it's probably not what he's thinking about for most of the day," says Polly Young-Eisendrath, Ph.D., clinical associate professor of psychiatry at the University of Vermont medical college in Burlington.

And men tend to blame their environment for their weight—"Those darn business lunches!"—instead of themselves, as women do.

Men also don't have the double bind. "If he offers a competent, confident way of being, he'll be seen as attractive even if he isn't *physically* attractive," says Dr. Young-Eisendrath.

as a backlash to the women's movement," says Raether. "When you're emaciated and anorexic, you can't be a strong, powerful person."

Today, the ideal woman is both thin and large-breasted. "But let's face it—women who weigh 90 pounds usually don't wear a 36C bra," says Diana Zuckerman, Ph.D., executive director of the National Center for Policy Research for Women and Families in Washington, D.C. We're striving for an unnatural ideal. And

our bodies are still a very crucial part of how we're judged by others (and by ourselves), which puts an awful lot of stress on us.

Perpetrator #2: The Media

The saying has been beaten into our psyches: "No woman can be too rich or too thin." And, thanks to plastic surgery and computer-enhanced photos, flawless women stare back at us in every media form.

"Compared to 20, 40, or 60 years ago, few actresses have large noses, heavy thighs, or flat chests," says Dr. Zuckerman. And a study in the *International Journal of Eating Disorders* revealed that blind women are happier with their bodies than sighted women, so visions of these unrealistic role models clearly have an impact.

"These bodies (we see in the media) rarely appear in nature," says Dr. Zuckerman, "but women still feel inadequate and unattractive in comparison."

And while models are shrinking, the average woman is getting larger. The models for *Playboy* centerfolds have been getting smaller since 1959, and since 1980, 99 percent of them have been underweight. Meanwhile, outside magazine pages, busts and waistlines are an inch bigger than they were 10 years ago—bringing the average dress size up to 14.

A study in the journal *Sex Roles* revealed that this growing gap in size between models and real women has made average-size women feel dissatisfied with their bodies and, hence, very stressed.

Perpetrator #3: The Double Bind

Try hard to look good and please everyone and you'll probably be liked, but you'll sacrifice many of your own needs and desires along the way. On the flip side, if you take responsibility for your own decisions and stand up for yourself, you run the risk of being called a bitch.

In essence, we're damned if we do and damned if we don't. Because of this double bind, there's an emphasis on power through appearance rather than through self-determination and actions, says Polly Young-Eisendrath, Ph.D., clinical associate professor of psychiatry at the University of Vermont Medical College in Burlington, and author of *Women and Desire: Beyond Wanting to Be Wanted*.

As a result, some women see thinness as a sign of competence. "Many doors are open to women today, but unfortunately some women aren't so eager to rush through them—they're still too concerned with their appearances," Dr. Young-Eisendrath says. And some women never work out this confusion, remaining caught up in this obsession concerning appearance even into their later years.

"This is a very big problem that leads to an enormous amount of suffering for some women," she says.

There's nothing I hate more than bathing suit shopping.
—Retired secretary, grandmother, age 78

Perpetrator #4: Youth-Obsessed Society

The inevitable aging process affects women differently depending on their generation. "Women over 60 didn't grow up with TV, and research shows more of them are happy with their bodies," says Dr. Young-Eisendrath.

A woman under 60, however, is more likely to view the aging process as if it were a waiflike twentysomething trying to buy her husband a drink. And the media feeds on the baby boomer's antiaging craze, with ads exhorting, "Get your young body back with plastic surgery."

"There's now a medical term for sagging breasts—'breast ptosis'—like they're a disease," says Dr. Zuckerman.

Yet women who continue to obsess over their appearance into their forties and fifties will eventually learn that it's a losing game. "There's just no way you can look 25 all your life," says Dr. Young-Eisendrath.

I wish I had more of a chin. I'm a chinless wonder.
—Teacher, age 52

Reaping the Results: The Dangers of a Poor Body Image

These dangers include:

Distorted views. Some women become obsessed with imagined flaws to the point of avoiding public appearances—a disorder called *body dysmorphic disorder* (BDD). Women with BDD focus on their perceived flaws: skin problems, a large nose, or an asymmetrical face, for example. "And the more a woman stares at her flaw, the more obvious it becomes to her," says Andrea Allen, Ph.D., assistant professor of psychology at Mount Sinai School of Medicine in New York. It makes her self-conscious, less friendly, and it can make a lot of the things she feared the flaw would cause in the first place come true, such as social isolation.

Eating disorders. Some women avoid food (anorexia) or binge and purge (bulimia) in their attempt to be thin. "Eating disorders can

REAL-LIFE SCENARIO

She Hates Her Body

Marlene, 47, has taken a look at herself in the mirror and doesn't like what she sees. Her breasts sag, her stomach droops, her neck is crinkled, and her laugh lines are enough to make her cry. If only she could afford plastic surgery, she knows she'd be happy. Until then, she dresses in large, tentlike clothes to hide her perceived flaws and turns down social engagements because she doesn't want to be seen in public. What should she do?

Marlene's perception of herself seems to be dependent solely on her body image. And, as with alcohol, drugs, or gambling, this dependency is not healthy.

For some reason, Marlene feels inferior and consumed by shame to the point of social withdrawal, which is pretty serious. It may be that she can't accept the natural aging process. If this is true, then breast implants and a tummy tuck aren't going to remedy the problem. If she doesn't fix what's wrong in her *mind,* she'll just want to tuck something else later on. She needs to stop denying that she's getting older.

If, at age 47, Marlene is so preoccupied with her appearance that she can't go out in public or attend social events, she should probably get some therapy. The more she avoids facing her flaws by covering them up with big clothing and staying at home, the harder it will be for her to go out in public. At her age, she should feel a lot freer of appearance-related restrictions. Also, her body image problem could be a manifestation of something more serious, like depression or an anxiety disorder, which requires investigation.

If her problems go unchecked, Marlene's social withdrawal will eventually take its toll on her relationships.

Experts consulted
Edie Raether
Licensed psychotherapist
Raleigh, North Carolina

Polly Young-Eisendrath, Ph.D.
Clinical associate professor of psychiatry
University of Vermont Medical College
Burlington

threaten mental and physical health and even lead to death," says Margaret Chesney, Ph.D., professor of medicine at the University of California, San Francisco, and a principal investigator on women's stress for the National Institute of Mental Health. Among other dangers, a woman may become infertile, or constant vomiting may cause her teeth to fall out or lead to cancer of the esophagus. And recurrent yo-yo dieting can strain the heart and increase the risk of gallbladder disease.

Weight gain. Some women turn to food when they get stressed out about body image, leading to weight gain. "Ironically, we might be more successful and weigh less collectively if we didn't have the 'thinness norm,' " says Dr. Chesney.

Depression. As diet after diet fails, a woman may decide thinness is an unattainable dream and become depressed. "The depression and stress can cause insomnia, drinking, and other habits that can harm health," says Dr. Zuckerman.

Increased illness. Any kind of stress harms the body, and stress over body image is no exception. It weakens the immune system, making you more likely to get sick. "If you're worried about your appearance, it can cause you to do damaging things like overexercising or undergoing too many surgeries on top of the general stress associated with unhappiness," says Dr. Allen.

Loss of sexual self. "Many women are so focused on looking sexy that they never learn to feel sexual pleasure and they don't enjoy sex," says Dr. Young-Eisendrath. In order to have good orgasms, you have to forget about your appearance, relax, and let go.

Decreased memory. Dieting and the stress of dieting have been shown to impair a woman's mental capacity as much as having two drinks.

My stomach is like a separate being—I call it Bubba.
—College student, age 19

Learning to Love Your Body— Cellulite and All

In order to lower the stress a negative body image causes, we have to accept and respect our whole selves (complete with warts, mousy hair, or short legs), and recognize that our power lies in our abilities, not in our appearance.

Please yourself. "Pay attention to how much time and effort you put into wanting to be desired by others," says Dr. Young-Eisendrath. Ask yourself what you *really* want out of life. If it's your doctorate in physics, for example, channel more of your energy there and less into making yourself over into some glossy magazine image. "You have to either tune your energy in to what kinds of effects you think you're having on others, or you have to tune in to what's actually going on in your subjective experience—you can't be both places at once," she says.

Avoid mirrors. "If you make it a point to look in the mirror more than three times a day, you should probably cut down, because it could become obsessive," says Dr. Allen. "Get dressed, put on your makeup, try to look your best, and then walk away," she says.

End comparisons. A lot of women compare themselves to other women. "And they'll compare themselves to models in a magazine, or they'll walk into a room, pick out the most gorgeous woman, and compare themselves to her. It's very self-defeating," says Dr. Allen. So, if looking through magazines makes you feel bad, stop doing it. Or subscribe to a magazine for larger women. And keep in mind that women in movies and magazines have people with brushes and combs waiting off-camera, ready to pounce on an out-of-place hair or a makeup smudge.

Also, if you find yourself thinking traffic-stopping good looks are the ticket to success, take a look around. Check out former Attorney General Janet Reno and former Secretary of State Madeleine Albright—both smart, successful women, but hardly beauty queens. "You can be attractive and interested in your appearance, as long as you know you aren't your appearance and you don't spend most of your time and effort there," says Dr. Young-Eisendrath.

Don't put yourself down. We've all done the glance-in-a-mirror shot-to-the-self "Yuck! You look like a bomb hit you." "But every time you criticize yourself (even if you're doing it in jest), you program your mind to think negatively about your appearance," says Raether. "One of the greatest powers of our being is that we can choose our own thoughts," she says. So choose good ones. Next time you start to bash your hair, stop and look for a positive: "Wow! My eyes look really blue today" or "This dress really flatters me."

Join forces with the enemy. Despite societal messages that fuel competition between women, women can actually be very supportive and empowering to one another. "We just need reinforcement," says Raether. So join a women's support group or book club. Read women's books and talk about them. Or just get together and talk about your lives over some wine or coffee.

Remember your health. The message isn't to veg on the couch, eat everything in sight, be 50 pounds overweight, and feel good about it. "In order to have a healthy body image, you have to have a healthy body," says Raether. Eat well, but get out there and exercise, "not just to lose weight, but to be healthy and to feel the exhilaration of being alive," she says.

The Fifth Circle: Money and Finances

Your hand slips into the pocket of your winter coat on this, the first frigid day of the season, and you feel a slip of paper. Is it? Could it be? It is! Money!

Whoever said money can't buy happiness never won the lottery. True, there are the *things* money buys: wardrobes, cars, trips to Paris, gourmet dinners. But even more, money can buy calm, removing the stress of a million what-ifs, as in "What if the water heater breaks?" or "What if the car breaks down?" or "What if I get sick and can't work?"

But like a double-faced Janus, money has its darker side as a stress inducer. Money matters can be so stressful, in fact, that we have an easier time discussing issues such as orgasms and our children's bowel habits than we do our finances.

"And what do people fight about in relationships? Sometimes it may be in-laws, but most of the time it's money," says Virginia Morris, Ph.D., editorial director of Lightbulb Press in New York City and author of *A Woman's Guide to Investing*.

Financial stress affects us physically as well. A study reported in the *Journal of Periodontology* found that a high level of financial stress doubles your risk of gum disease because it taxes the immune system and makes you more likely to grind your teeth out of frustration and less likely to brush and floss.

But we can escape some of money's havoc if we understand the nature of the beast.

The Stressful Side of Money

"There are some women who are good at managing money—budgeting, saving, and investing—but there are still a great number of women who are very anxious about it," says Carrie Schwab Pomcrantz, vice president of consumer education at Charles Schwab and Company in San Francisco. In general, she and other experts say, money matters turn our hair gray because:

We're not socialized to handle it. "Our culture has traditionally divided things up into guy stuff and girl stuff—and money is guy stuff," says Ruth May, Ph.D., certified financial planner and professor at the graduate school of management at the University of Dallas. For instance, one study found that when parents discussed money with their daughters, they focused on soft topics, like saving and budgeting. When they talked to their sons, they discussed serious money stuff, like the stock market, estate planning, and wills. Because of this divide, women tend to take a backseat when it comes to money management, says Pomerantz.

We don't have as much of it. It's sad but true: Even in the 21st century, women still don't earn as much as men do. We hold more traditionally "pink collar," lower-paying positions, such as bank tellers, nurses, and secretaries. Even when we hold jobs comparable jobs to the menfolk, we still earn only 75 percent of what they do. At the same time, more of us are supporting ourselves—and our kids—on our own. "So women are often struggling with situations where there isn't enough money for all that is needed," a guaranteed stress inciter, says Irene Leech, Ph.D., associate professor of consumer education at Virginia Polytechnic University in Blacksburg.

We're intimidated by it. Many of us are confused when it comes to money issues because we haven't been exposed to financial information. In addition, financial methods and vehicles change fairly often, and in our busy lives it's difficult to keep up.

Overall, if you exhibit any of the following behaviors, you need to make some changes, say experts.

➧ Your husband makes all the financial decisions.

WOMAN TO WOMAN
She Overcame Her Own Money Problems

Olivia Mellan, 54, a psychotherapist in Washington, D.C., and author of Money Shy to Money Sure: A Woman's Road Map to Financial Well-Being, *counsels patients on money problems. One day, she realized she needed her own advice as much as her patients did—she was an overspender.*

I got into money therapy in 1982. I coined money personality types and dove into my patients' childhoods to uncover their money issues. In the process, I was forced to look at my own money issues.

My mother was a shopaholic. She bought clothing for herself when she was depressed or felt like celebrating. She hid the bags until my father was in a good mood. And she expressed her love for me by buying me clothes. I remember wishing she would express her love in other ways, but the clothes were better than nothing, so I developed a clothing addiction.

I used my credit card often and paid only the monthly minimum, oblivious to my skyrocketing balance. In my own way, I, too, hid bags. And my ex-husband was somewhat of a spender himself, so that didn't help matters.

Eighteen years ago, someone I was about to do a workshop with said: "Money is the last taboo in the therapist's office; people have a harder time talking about money than about sex or childhood trauma." After that statement, and while working with other people's money issues, I thought, "Hmmm—could I be hiding money issues?" I definitely was.

But the real saving grace was my second husband. He became a money mentor to me, saying, "It's ridiculous to pay 18 percent on a credit card each month—you should pay it off. If you can't, come to me and we'll work it out."

And so I stopped. I learned to build a bridge between my stressed-out state (when I would compulsively spend) and my non-stressed-out state through therapy, meditation, deep breathing, and talking to myself. That meant nourishing my core instead of indulging the surface—I got into things like ballroom dancing, spoof songwriting, and jewelry making. And I simply stayed out of the stores that tempted me.

WOMEN ASK WHY

Should I pay my bills online?

Thanks to the ever-expanding Internet, we can now pay our bills without lifting a pen. There are some real advantages to online bill paying—you can pay all your bills in a matter of minutes, and you don't have to pay for postage.

You have a few options when it comes to paying bills online. Often brick-and-mortar banks have their own online services, in which case you may not have to switch banks. You can also use a virtual, online-only bank, like Wingspan, at www.wingspanbank.com, for example. You can also use checkbook software, like Quicken, which offers online bill paying, printed checks, and a way to track your finances.

Online bill paying is relatively simple once you establish your billing accounts. After you log in with a secret password, you access a personalized list of bills the program will pay. Just click on the bill and the amount you want to pay, and money is transferred directly from your checking or savings account.

To select an online bank or financial site on which to pay your bills, check out its rating on one of the expert sites—like kiplinger.com or money.com—and choose a site that's ranked in the top three.

Expert consulted
Judith Briles, Ph.D.
Financial expert
Aurora, Colorado

- You find yourself getting frustrated and upset about money.
- You're always unpleasantly surprised at your credit card bill.
- You feel angry when you want to buy something but can't afford it.
- You shop when you're depressed or when you feel like celebrating.
- You go to the grocery store and spend at least $50 more than you planned.

Join the Ranks of the Money Savvy

With the numerous resources available these days, boosting your financial knowledge can be as easy as paying the electric bill. Before you begin, however, you need to change your overall attitude about money issues, says Dr. May.

"Many women have to do some emotional work before they can get educated on money matters—sort of reprogramming the mind to think it's not a taboo thing for women to be financially confident and in control. We have the careers—now it's time for us to take charge of what we earn from them," she says. Here's how.

Hit the books. And give yourself time to digest the information. She recommends:

- *Personal Finance for Dummies* by Eric Tyson, This is an easy read—clear, practical financial information.
- *One Up on Wall Street: How to Use What You Already Know to Make Money in the Market* by Peter Lynch. The book covers how stocks work and offers some commonsense ideas about money management.
- *Prince Charming Isn't Coming: How Women Get Smart about Money* by Barbara Stanny. The author turned her parents' inheritance over to her husband, who then lost it all in the stock market. She shares her experiences and advice. "The best book I've read about women and finances," says Dr. May.

Take a class. There are many beginner financial seminars offered through community colleges and universities. Investment firms also offer free programs and seminars. Just keep in mind that they may have some bias, says Judith Briles, financial expert in Aurora, Colorado, and author of *Ten Smart Money Moves for Women: How to Conquer Your Financial Fears.* "They want you to become a customer, but you can go to learn the basics."

Surf the Net. To find an online site, see what the pros recommend. Go to a Web site, like Kiplinger's (www.kiplinger.com), Money Magazine (www.money.com), or Gomez Advisors (www.gomez.com), that rates financial Web sites.

Hire a financial advisor. An advisor can oversee any financial moves you want to make (except taxes), from budgeting to estate planning. When you pick one, look for a fee-based planner, not one who works on commission, and check the advisor's credentials. A high-quality education, such as a bachelor's degree in finance or business from a reputable college or university, is more valuable than a lot of low-quality education, such as self-taught courses. The most common certifications/degrees are chartered financial analyst (CFA) and master of business administration (MBA).

Take Charge of Your Financial Life

The books and seminars provide the basics, but the hands-on money

ON THE FRONT LINES
A CPA

If you think money stresses you out, imagine the life of a certified public accountant (CPA) during tax season. Judith E. Dacey, a CPA in Orlando, Florida, has had to develop some effective strategies to handle the stress.

In the tax business, April 15 is the good news and the bad news—glad it's over, sorry it's gone. For Judith, it's very stressful, but it's also enjoyable.

"It's the time of the year when I get to catch up on the news of the personal lives of my clients—who graduated, who got scholarships, who changed jobs—and it's also the financial lifeblood of the business, like Christmas for the retailers," she says. "The main stress in the last few weeks comes from haranguing procrastinators so they won't knock on my door at midnight on April 14." Another stress is selecting which returns to file extensions on because the clock is winning the battle.

"Overall, the stress is three times greater than what I feel during the rest of the year," she says. Between February 1 and April 15, she works about 70 hours a week.

"I think my personality helps me deal with the stress. I am an even-tempered, upbeat person, and I genuinely enjoy meeting with my clients."

She also knows that even though she can't change the workload she has willingly created, she can at least control her attitude. So, during tax time, she gives herself permission to not be the perfect mother, wife, or entrepreneur.

"I let go of some responsibilities: I avoid outside meetings, I never obligate myself for committee or leadership work during tax season, and I essentially put business development on hold," she says. "I also pass projects to my staff. At home, I delegate more of the housekeeping chores, like buying groceries and doing laundry. I almost always take off Sundays to be with my family. And I laugh more—I watch late-night TV comedy, read funny books, see funny movies, and make jokes more often around the office."

management is up to you. To get started:

Eliminate large debts. "The worst thing in the world is to be in credit card debt to the point that you're paying only minimum payments," says Laurence I. Foster, certified public accountant, personal financial specialist, and tax partner at Richard A. Eisner and Company, LLP, a New York City–based accounting and consulting firm. "With the rates credit card companies charge, you'll never get out of debt." If you can't control yourself around your credit cards, make them less accessible. Keep one card for emergencies, such as your car's breaking down. Then toss that card in a drawer, give it to a friend, or put it in a small bowl of water and freeze it. "Waiting for it to thaw will give you time to think about your priorities," says Dr. Leech.

Save, save, save. Ideally, your emergency savings should equal about 5 to 10 percent of your total earnings.

Spend wisely. Don't go to the mall just for something to do. "Instead, do things with your friends and family, and take up some hobbies," says Dr. May. If you see something you really want, wait until the next day to buy it—if it sticks in your brain, you really want it.

Use ATM machines as little as possible. "Instead of pulling out the minimum $20, you pull out $40 or $60, and once you've got the cash, it goes to cash heaven—$3 frozen yogurts, $4 gourmet coffees—it's just too easy to spend," says Dr. Briles.

Invest for now. Some basic investing tips from the experts include the following:

- Get educated on the basics—what a stock is, what a bond is, and how they react to the market.

FINANCIAL DEFINITIONS

Sometimes investment and financial terms seem like one big bowl of alphabet soup. Here's the breakdown.

Individual Retirement Account (IRA). Uncle Sam allows you to save up to $2,000 a year from earned income in these accounts, investing it in many financial vehicles. With a traditional IRA, you don't pay taxes on the money until you withdraw it, starting at age 59½, and you must begin to take it out by age 70½. There may be limitations based on the amount of income that you earn. You can open an IRA at a bank, an insurance company, or a brokerage house.

A Roth IRA works a bit differently. You pay taxes on the money when it goes into the account, but it grows tax-free, so there's no tax bill when you take it out at age 70½. It's different from a regular IRA in that you can still continue to make contributions after age 70½. Whether you should choose a traditional IRA or a Roth depends on how long you have until retirement. Someone closer to retirement should choose a traditional IRA, because in order to withdraw your money from a Roth tax-free, the money has to be in the account at least five years.

The following are investments (ranked from least to most risky).

Certificate of deposit (CD). Basically, you're lending money to the bank. The longer you let the bank hold on to your money, the higher the interest rate the bank pays you. CDs are insured (up to $100,000) by the Federal Depository Insurance Corporation (FDIC), a government insurance company. So if the bank that issued the CD goes out of business, the FDIC will pay your principle and interest payments up to $100,000 per bank.

- Split your investments among various financial securities, such as stocks, bonds, and certificates of deposit (CDs)—this is called "asset allocation."
- Invest in a diversified stock portfolio—have a lot of different stocks in different business areas, such as technology, financial, and health care, so if one sector hits

Money market. A mutual fund that invests in low-risk, short-term vehicles, such as government bonds or CDs. It's a very conservative, liquid investment, so it can be used to hold savings. At most institutions you can write checks from your money market account or use an automatic teller machine (ATM) card. (Some firms have minimum check amounts as high as $5,000, so ask about restrictions.)

Bond. With this, you're essentially lending money to a company or government entity to help it raise cash. The company promises to provide a certain interest rate on your money and to repay it, plus the interest accrued, on a certain date. If you buy a municipal bond, you're lending money to a municipality; government bonds lend money to the government, and so on. Some government and municipal bonds may be tax-free.

Mutual fund. This is a conglomeration of stocks, bonds, and/or money market instruments all wrapped up into one investment vehicle (and one quarterly statement). Because your money is spread among various investments, it's less risky than putting all your cash into one place, such as all stocks or all bonds. Your money is pooled with that of other investors, and a mutual fund manager decides what to buy.

Stocks. Here, you own shares of a company, and your money shrinks and grows depending on the value of that company and the supply-and-demand conditions of the stock market. Stock prices fluctuate in the short term, but as the company grows, the price may grow in the long term. Of course, there's always a chance prices could drop, so there is some risk.

hard times, your entire portfolio isn't decimated.
- Consider an automatic investment plan, in which money is automatically deducted from your checking or savings account and invested wherever you choose.
- Forget day trading. This involves the rapid buying and selling of stocks, a not-so-smart investment technique. "If you day trade, you'll lose your money—it's like gambling," says Dr. Briles.

Invest for later. You need to save for retirement—regardless of what your husband does.

If you have one, invest in your 401(k) or 403(b) at work and in an Individual Retirement Account (IRA).

Put It All Together: Write a Budget

You may hate the word, but it's a necessary evil. To be financially stable, you must be able to cover your basic necessities without worry while at the same time reducing debt and building savings. Hence the B-word.

"To get over the biggest hurdle, write it down—putting it on paper gives you a sense of empowerment," says Dr. May. Here are her step-by-step recommendations.

1. Write down your net monthly take-home pay. Then make a list of your expenses and rank them from "must pays" (like the mortgage and car payment) to "could pay next month," then subtract the most important first. Include in this section expenses like groceries and gas.
2. Subtract large payments toward any credit card debt you're carrying, maybe $100 or $200 a month.
3. Subtract a set amount for savings, even if it's only $25 a week.
4. The remaining amount is what's left over for fun stuff—movies, dinners out, that killer pair of red shoes. "Post that total on your bathroom mirror, or wherever you're going to see it and remember it—and don't go over it," says Dr. May.

The Sixth Circle: Love and Marriage

"To the moon, Alice!"

Marital relationships have come a long way since the heyday of *The Honeymooners*. And yet . . . just *how* far have we come? Women are taking a larger role in the workplace, but we're still left holding the household bag. Some men are now equal partners in child rearing and household upkeep, but most are not. Firm ideas about gender roles are starting to break apart, yet those splinters can be painful.

The people who taught us everything we know about relationships—our parents—didn't have access to the wide range of choices we have, so our ideas about love are a mix of their old status quo and our new menu of options. While men and women consciously know the sky's the limit, we all want it to be *our* sky.

So what one might see as puffy white clouds of equality and teamwork, the other might see as dark clouds of lost identity and exploitation. When these two fronts come together, storms start brewing and battles break out.

The key to making your marriage work? Let it rain.

"Conflict is our only means to intimacy," says Judith Sherven, Ph.D., a clinical psychologist in Windham, New York, and coauthor of *The New Intimacy: Discovering the Magic at the Heart of Your Differences*. Whenever two people join their lives, tensions inevitably erupt, she says. You have one relationship, but as two individuals, you see the world in two very distinct ways. Seeing this push-and-pull, this stress, as a positive force for growth will take you much further in minimizing it altogether. "When you argue with your spouse, it shows you trust each other enough to divulge your true needs—it's the fertilizer the relationship needs to grow."

What You're Really Fighting About

It ain't the dishes.

When you start railing at your husband for leaving a wet towel on the floor or not listening when you talk, it always comes down to the same issue: your needs.

"From the day we are born, we try to satisfy our needs," says Allen Fay, M.D., psychiatrist in New York City and author of *Making It as a*

PREMARITAL COUNSELING: WHY TO DO IT AND HOW IT WORKS

People from all over the world buy *Consumer Reports* each year to weigh the pros and cons of every purchase, from a toaster to a toilet.

Yet only a small fraction of us put our prospective mates through the same rigorous checklists. "It's too unromantic," we think. "Love conquers all," we hum.

Hmm . . . a $15 appliance vs. the rest of our earthbound life. You'd think we'd do a little more intensive research first!

That's what premarital counseling is: a chance to kick the tires of your relationship, twist all the knobs of your communication skills, make sure you really know what you're getting on this bill of sale. "So many people are on their best behavior when they're courting—then they get married and wonder why their needs aren't met," says Judith Sherven, Ph.D., a clinical psychologist in Windham, New York, and coauthor of *The New Intimacy: Discovering the Magic at the Heart of Your Differences.* "If you bring up issues right at the beginning, you'll see if your partner is willing to come forward and deal with them."

Premarital counseling provides a forum for the major questions that will inevitably strain your life: child rearing, sex, extended family relationships . . . how many times you'll be expected to sit through Super Bowl replays without having a nervous breakdown.

What it's not is therapy. "Some people think 'therapy' is voodoo, or you really have to be sick in order to go," says Dr. Sherven. "We don't call it therapy—most people need education, training, and coaching."

Dr. Sherven and her husband, Jim Sniechowski, Ph.D., work as a team with couples before they get married. They ask about already existing trouble spots, then examine how each person views the marriage of his or her own parents—the blueprints from which we all work.

Armed with this info, the counselors coach the couple in conflict-resolution skills by guiding them through discussions in the office and giving them homework to work on alone.

The next step is often the hardest. "So many people don't know how to receive love," says Dr. Sniechowski. "Somehow, they think, when real love comes around, they'll know the difference." The doctors help them "discover a place within themselves for that love to land," says Dr. Sherven.

The third issue is crucial: the couple has to agree to leave behind their allegiances to their original family. "You can be legally married, but you'll never be spiritually married until you step away and say, 'This is who we are and the family we're going to build,' " says Dr. Sniechowski. "That may mean difficulty with in-laws, but that has to take place for the marriage to be solid."

Most couples come for 10 to 20 sessions. By the time they get married, they have formulated a set of guiding principles to help them through their tough times. Those principles can have a place in the couple's ceremony: the vows.

"If you've written your vows, you're personally committing to what you're saying to each other," says Dr. Sniechowski. "Instead of merely repeating words, you really believe them."

Couple: Prescription for a Quality Relationship.

Still, there are certain similarities in what we fight about. They typically come down to the following:

Sex. Sexual problems often get swept under the rug because one or both of you are too embarrassed to bring it up. But sexual satisfaction is one of the determining factors of your marriage's likelihood of success, so developing a means to talk about it is in your best interest.

Money. Money is a way to prove worth, present ourselves to the world, secure our freedom, and provide for our family. One partner may be a tightwad, the other a spendthrift. "There is simply no way that you could ever have exactly the same concept of, approach to, and connection to money as your partner," says Albert Couch, founding partner of Signal Tree Resolutions mediation center in Akron, Ohio, and mediator of more than 1,200 family and organization negotiations.

Children. No matter how stress-free your relationship was prechildren, having kids demands time management and an emotional support that even the most rock-solid relationships find challenging. One study traced 93 couples over 10 years and found that raising small children was one of the biggest factors in the decline of their marriage.

Outside relationships. Aside from infidelity—which has its own host of problems—many couples fight about outside friendships, which can bring up issues of abandonment. Yet although we may imagine our spouse filling all our emotional and social needs, that's an impossible expectation.

Extended family. One of the most common

WOMAN TO WOMAN
Counseling Strengthened Her Marriage

For 10 years, Ming Lu, 47, and her husband were locked in a never-ending competition over who gave more to the relationship. Now married 18 years and with two children, Ming credits marriage counseling with bringing happiness to their marriage. This is her story.

I got pregnant 3 months after we were married. We enjoyed our first year together, but when our daughter was born, we took an immediate nosedive. Issues like security, values, and religion—all those things that we could sweep under the rug before—now came to the surface. Yet we hadn't developed the communication tools to deal with them. I come from a Chinese background of emotional suppression and quiet obedience; my husband also didn't stick up for himself. We'd entered the marriage with those patterns.

I spent the next 10 years feeling resentful. He was gone all day, and I felt stuck with the responsibility for the house, my daughter, and the son born 6 years later. If I wanted to get a job, I had to find child care, and I felt I couldn't ask him for help. That's my pattern—I clean up after everybody's mess and then feel resentful about it.

After doing that for 10 years, I decided I wanted a life. That's when we started seeing the marriage counselors. We saw a couple, so the male therapist focused on my husband and the woman focused on me.

In the second session of counseling, we degenerated into the same argument we always have—one of us saying the

family conflicts in any marriage pits a husband's mother against his wife. Each woman wants proof that *she* is more important, and if he can't stand up to his mom, an inevitable triangle results. Ethnic differences about the degree of extended family involvement can also be a huge stressor, especially when it comes to spending the couple's most precious resource: time.

Housework. Almost one in three of us with

other wasn't doing enough. I'd say, "I have to work double because you made us buy this house in this expensive area." He'd say, "We needed the house because you insisted your mother live with us after the second child." We went back and forth like that, accusing each other.

When we stopped, the therapists smiled and told us it was the classic gender war. We didn't realize it was so common. Just hearing that was a relief. They said that marriage roles are changing and that when one party breaks out of a role, the other feels threatened.

We also talked about how I felt that his priorities took precedence over mine. I was surprised to find he felt the same way. The therapists helped us see we both felt like second-class citizens because we didn't know how to feel like first-class citizens. That's what we were taught when we were children, and we were recreating that feeling.

I think one of the benefits of the marriage therapy was being able to see the other person's point of view—we saw that understanding takes away a lot of anger and resentment. If I'm clear about my boundaries, I don't have to be resentful, and it enables him to be clear about his. That was a major discovery.

After therapy, I started immediately articulating when something doesn't feel right. When we talk about it right away, I don't store things up.

We fall back into old patterns sometimes, especially when we're busy, but I'm really happy now. Our therapists didn't tell us how to fix it—they made us aware so we could identify problems and deal with them ourselves.

kids works outside the home, yet the dishes and laundry still have to get done—usually by us. Although women typically perform more than 70 percent of the housework, researchers found the ideal split is actually 45.8 percent each (the remaining 10 per cent should be farmed out or forgotten entirely).

Infertility. Having children may be a great stress on a marriage, but not being able to have them may be even greater. Almost 1 in 10 couples has problems conceiving, and this experience may result in lowered self-esteem, increased depression and anxiety, and feelings of guilt or shame. This issue can spill over into couples' sex lives, financial plans (due to the high cost of fertility treatments), and reenvisioning future plans.

Spirituality. Before you were married, your different belief systems may have seemed exotic. But now that you're debating charitable donations or whether your kids light menorah candles or set cookies out for Santa, your faith takes on a little more weight.

Work. Couples today work an average of 1,000 more hours a year than couples did 30 years ago. We bring this overload and our workplace slights home with us and, if we're not careful, infect the very place that's supposed to be our safe haven.

Health. Health is one of the top three stresses women have throughout their lives, and many women function as the gatekeepers for their entire family's health. Smoking, alcoholism, and other physical and mental health problems can be divisive issues. Watching a person you love refuse to take care of himself—or deflecting his ever-watchful eye when he's hounding you—can be stressful, but at its root is a fear of abandonment.

Turn Conflict into Caring

Just knowing that inside your marital stress lie the keys to greater intimacy can move you toward peace. The following skills can help you find that inner harmony. And while new conflicts will inevitably arise, when they do, you'll have more practice in resolving them easily and peacefully.

Fake it. If you can't seem to resolve the current issue, call a 1-week truce. "Behavior can precede change," says Dr. Fay. "Some couples need no more than a few style changes to bring about marked and lasting improvement in their relationship." Pretend you've solved the problem, and add a compliment and a couple of long hugs every day. How angry do you feel now?

Give him the good news first. "For most couples, the tone of the evening is set by the homecoming greeting," says Dr. Fay. Tell him about your daughter's fantastic report card before broaching the subject of mortgage payments— the rest of your evening together will be rosier for it.

Take compliments. "Most of us have trouble receiving compliments, but just accepting them, without protest, can allow us to see another person's point of view," says James Sniechowski, Ph.D., a relationship trainer and consultant in Windham, New York, and coauthor of *The New Intimacy: Discovering the Magic at the Heart of Your Differences.*

Use fuzzy math. "A marriage isn't a 50/50 proposition," says Dr. Fay. "It's a 60/60 proposition—each person has to do a little more than what he thinks his share is." Keeping score will slowly eat away at your happiness.

Use your "I" to focus. "Your feelings are the only pieces of information you bring to the discussion," says Dr. Sherven. Talk about anything, as long as you preface it with "When *I* see you doing this, *I* feel . . . ," rather than "*You* always. . . ."

Give him reminders. Your anniversary is coming up and you're afraid he's forgotten. Don't be coy—remind him, says Dr. Fay. Sound unromantic? That's all-or-nothing thinking. "If you're saying things to yourself like 'I shouldn't have to ask him' or 'If he cared about me, he'd

remember,' those are sure signs that you're afraid to stand up for your own needs," says Dr. Sherven.

While you're at it, leave yourself a couple of reminders like "Tell Bill I love him." These reminders help you both develop loving habits.

Kill the past. The past is valuable in only two ways: recalling pleasant experiences and learning from mistakes, says Dr. Fay. "If a deed was bad enough for you to end the relationship, by all means do so," he says. "But if you choose to stay with your partner, tell yourself to forget it, and don't hassle him." Harboring resentment about the past only destroys what you could have in the present and future.

Write it down. A good way to get started talking about any issue is to share what it means to you, says Dr. Sniechowski. Write the words "Money (or sex or friendship or religion) means . . ." Then write, "When my parents talked about money, they . . ." and "My first memory of what money means was . . ." Write any images, phrases, memories, and priorities you choose. Compare the lists and ask questions. Any negotiation will benefit from this shared information, he says.

Don't compromise. If both people give up something they don't want to give up, they'll just feel resentful, says Dr. Sherven. Don't give in. Instead, work toward a third way, a creative solution that satisfies the both of you.

Use the 10-second rule. When you're in a discussion, especially if it's a heated argument, wait 10 seconds before responding. "The 10-second rule slows the mind down a little bit and puts a pause into our interaction with each other," says Couch. "If I have to wait before I respond, I'll listen; I won't be thinking about what I'm going to say because I'll have 10 seconds to do that."

Turn threats into promises. Although you may issue threats like "If you do that one more time, I'll leave you," such verbiage ultimately weakens your relationship and causes mistrust on both sides. Protect yourself without creating resentment by calmly and clearly stating your feelings and how you intend to act in the future, says Dr. Fay: "It's upsetting to me when you come home drunk. I've decided that in the future, I will go to my mother's until you sober up."

Just bring it up. If you resist even thinking about an issue, start there. "Say, 'I'm afraid to talk about sex,'" says Couch. Whatever you're most afraid of discussing is exactly what you need to talk about the most, he says.

Put it into words. "If you really loved me, you would . . ." Writing down these unspoken statements explicitly is a quick way to get to the heart of your needs, says Margaret Paul, Ph.D., a counselor in Los Angeles. Write down everything that comes to mind—this will always come in handy for you both as a reference for each other. (You may be surprised by how many overlap with your partner.)

Become your husband's student. Ask him how he feels about our place in the universe or who he thinks will win the Series this year, and drink in everything he's saying as if you have to repeat it back verbatim. "Most often when couples fight, they are trying to protect themselves—they don't want to be controlled or rejected," says Dr. Paul. "When they move into an in-

---

On the Front Lines
A Marriage Counselor

Marriage counselors are a special breed. Just picture an average weekday for Shirley Glass, Ph.D., a clinical psychologist in Baltimore. She sees patients from 8:00 A.M. to noon, followed by several hours of writing for one of the two books she has in the works, capped off with a few evening sessions, completing her day by 9:00 P.M. Fridays and weekends are devoted to full-time writing. In addition, she stays on top of developments in her field, researches her specialty (infidelity), and leads workshops around the country.

"If I actually totaled up my hourly wage, including writing, I think it would come out to ½ cent per hour," she jokes. "It can be exhausting."

Patience is a counselor's stock in trade, as well as compassion. "If I don't feel compassion for someone, it's very hard to treat them," Dr. Glass says. Often in marital counseling, one of the partners can be more stubborn and unwilling to change, which can make sustaining energy (and compassion) challenging.

After many years in the business, Dr. Glass still finds it hard to accept that she can't help everyone. "Some people just don't want to become healthy. I learned that long ago, but I'm still working on accepting it," she says.

When she works with individuals, she feels more optimistic because her patient is there willingly, hoping to grow as a person, so there's usually more trust and openness. When she's working with couples, however, the supportive process becomes a little trickier—she has to be vigilant with herself to make sure she's fair to both parties.

Working as a team with a male colleague can make this a bit easier, especially when things get heated. "I've heard plenty of 'F-yous,' no matter who's around," says Dr. Glass.

Most of the healing with couples goes on behind the scenes, she says, once they leave her office. When it happens, though, couples can't hide it—seeing them sitting closer to each other, touching each other and smiling, always makes her happy.

"That's the most gratifying part of my job," she says.

tention to *learn*—about themselves, their fears, their beliefs, each other—it doesn't take very long to resolve conflict."

Encourage him to watch the game. Although it may seem like it takes time away from your togetherness, pursuing personal interests is one of the best ways to support your marriage. "In the best relationships, partners are protective and supportive of each other's cherished activities and encourage each other to do their own thing," says Dr. Fay. Enjoying himself means he'll have more joy to bring to you.

Put some privacy back into your life. "It's amazing how many couples don't have locks on their bedroom doors," says Dr. Fay. List all the ways the outside world—including your kids—intrudes on your couple time, then find ways to keep them out.

Get help. With the laundry, that is. "I've saved a lot of dual-career marriages by just advising them to get household help," says Dr. Paul. It's not a cop-out—it's an investment in your relationship.

Don't wait for him. If you've gotten this far and you're shaking your head because you doubt your partner is ready, you're not off the hook yet—any of these tips will work even if you do them alone. "Just by making one small change, you change the entire system of your relationship," says Dr. Paul. "Setting your own boundaries and defining your own needs are the best ways to help him set his."

The Seventh Circle: The Kids

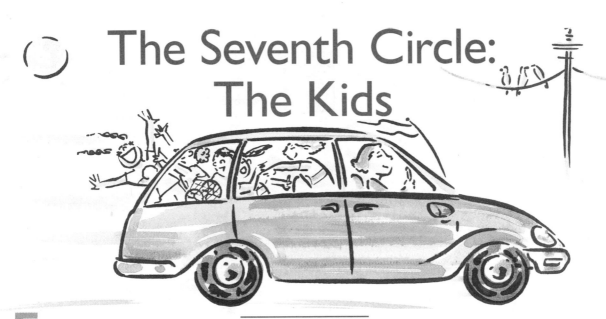

From that first, sleepless night when baby comes home from the hospital to that endless night when the 16-year-old stays out with the car until dawn, kids add stress to our lives. Think about it. How many times have you fled the house—whether to take a drive or a walk or just sit in the car and cry—because you couldn't face another battle over chores, another fight over curfew, another sibling argument? It's not surprising, then, that novels about women who suddenly walk away from their families are popular among middle-aged women with kids.

Thankfully, most of us don't leave. But children—for all that we love them—cause strains that are very real. Mastering relationships with them is made all the more difficult because it's not like riding a bike. It's not a skill we learn and then retain for life. Just when we think we have it figured out, the kids change. Seemingly overnight they go from bottle-feeding to drinking and driving. From lost teeth to lost virginity. Yet we have to learn how to handle these challenges if we're going to thrive instead of just survive.

While there's no one-size-fits-all solution to this often out-of-control part of your life, there are certain constants that can bring a sense of calm and control.

The Keys to Calm Parenting

Isn't it ironic that many of us spend weeks in childbirth classes to prepare for the first day of our child's life but rarely get any training to prepare us for the next 18 years? It gets even more difficult when our kids hit the tempestuous years of adolescence, when their primary development task becomes achieving independence.

So we polled child behavior and parenting specialists—including parents—on their recommendations for what we'll call Prevention's Guide to Calm Parenting.

Spend time with your child. Set a date for breakfast once a week with your teenager. Take your third grader out for an ice cream sundae. Maybe your daughter is worried about her weight. Instead of chastising her about obsessing, suggest the two of you walk together after dinner. Connect on what you have in common because too often it will feel like you have nothing in common at all, says Vickie Beck, a nurse/psychotherapist and consultant to Mercy Hospital in Baltimore.

Listen, listen, listen. Scheduling time with your kids isn't enough. You have to listen, Beck says. Stop cooking dinner, talking on the phone, paying bills, and just listen. Listening shows you respect their feelings and bolsters their self-esteem. And don't interrupt, even if your teenager lets slip a curse word or tells you something a friend did that you don't approve of. Right now you need to hear what they're *saying*, rather than worrying about *how* they're saying it.

Other listening suggestions.

- ➤ Watch as well as listen.
- ➤ Rephrase your child's words or ask her to break it down to be sure you understand.
- ➤ If you can't listen immediately, set a time when you can.
- ➤ If you disagree, do so respectfully, not insultingly.

Maintain a sense of humor. If you can't step back and see the absurdity of a situation, you won't survive parenthood, says Deborah Antony of Norfolk, Virginia. And she knows children and survival. Antony, 48, has homeschooled each of her four daughters—ages 10 through 18—through sixth grade while running a home-based day care and leading the board of her church's day care center.

With teenagers, everything is a drama, Antony says. You can buy into it and drive yourself nuts. Or you can just relax and go along for the ride.

Humor also helps her deal more calmly with other people's children. For instance, one day while she was watering her garden, the children in her care ran out into the yard, despite her warnings to stay away. Of course, they fell and got muddy. She could have blown up at them.

WOMAN TO WOMAN

She Found a Way to Cope with Her Troubled Daughter

Several years ago, when her oldest daughter began having significant behavior problems, Mary Flachsenhaar Kirsch, 52, a Norfolk, Virginia, mother of three, found it took the help of family, friends, church, and professionals—as well as antidepressants—to help her cope. Here is her story.

Just a few short years ago, my biggest concern was whether my three bright daughters would get the best teachers. Emily, the oldest, particularly excelled at everything she tried—violin, art, creative writing, running—and was very loving.

When Emily hit seventh grade, however, the problems began. She started going to parties, her attitude shifted, her grades fell. Her junior year in high school, she ran away to New York City. For 36 hellish hours, we didn't know if she was even alive. She came back, but the problems didn't stop. The next fall, she had to be hospitalized for life-threatening eating disorders. Her grades were bad and her self-esteem worse, but we were dealing with the life-and-death issue first.

Emily is 21 now, and we're still going through scares as she tries to find her way in an adult world. She's wrecked the car and had her driver's license suspended; she's worked at eight restaurants, had serious problems with roommates, and made a couple of false starts at college. A year ago she un-

Instead, she turned the hose on them and rinsed them off—clothes and all. The children stood dumbfounded for a minute, then started laughing and playing.

Touch them. Hug them, smooth their hair, tickle them. The human touch is de-stressing, not only to our kids but to us as well.

Set realistic rules and stick to them. If we hold our children accountable and make them earn privileges, they'll respect us for it, says Katherine Kersey, Ph.D., professor of education and chair of the department of child studies at Old Dominion University in Norfolk, Virginia.

derwent counseling and electroconvulsive therapy. That seems to have calmed some of her impulsivity, enough so that she can stay home peacefully now.

We've spent a small fortune on counseling; I've doubled the dosage of my antidepressant. But I have learned to lighten up on myself and my other daughters.

My husband and I take the "whole village" approach to raising kids. With no family here, though, we had to build our own village. I joined the Unitarian church about 3 years ago to duplicate that feeling of family and to be nurtured. Being part of that community gives me a lot of peace. And it provides a structure to get my children involved in family activities and community programs.

I've formed strong friendships with women in my age group and enjoy the support of families in similar circumstances. I've taken myself out of situations where the appearance and accomplishments of your kids are the most important measure of your worth. I jog about five times a week, and I stay up an hour or two after everyone else is asleep to read and find some peace and calm.

I think I would've self-destructed if I hadn't gone back to work full-time a couple of years ago. Having a job where I can succeed on my own is important. You have to get a life—a job, a volunteer effort, a hobby, a passion, something totally out of the realm of your kids. Something for you.

For instance, Dr. Kersey had a rule that her children had to make their beds before they could play outside. Two of her children made their beds each morning, while the other waited to see if it was raining after school. If it was raining, he concluded that he didn't have to make his bed that day. The rule was firm, but it provided some latitude.

Respect individuality and choice. Children are often frustrated by decisions that are made for them—about school, social activities, chores, and responsibilities. Wherever possible, provide options. For instance, Dr. Kersey recalls a couple who signed up their son for another season of Little League even though he didn't want to play. When his mother told him they'd signed him up, the boy left the room in a huff, muttering, "I wish I could sign *you* up for something!" Instead, Dr. Kersey says, while we should help our children discover their natural gifts, talents, and passions, we shouldn't push. "I've spoken to many mothers who bemoaned the fact that their daughters would not practice the piano," she says. "I ask, 'Why is she taking piano?' The answer: 'Because I always wished that I had taken piano and always vowed to give my daughter that opportunity.' So I suggested *they* take piano. Three mothers took me up on it."

Let go gradually. By the time children are teenagers, parents can't and shouldn't control their every action. Yet their need for independence is constantly warring with our need for assurance that they're ready to be on their own. Take cues from your children, says Beck. For instance, if your child isn't very responsible, you don't have to agree to his request for a weekend skiing trip. Instead, offer to take him to the slopes for the day and pick him up at a certain time.

Provide logical consequences. If you overreact, you take away a child's sense of hope. Beck knew one mother who pulled her daughter off the drill team, the girl's favorite activity, when her grades slipped, and she forbade her to rejoin until the following year. The girl was furious and started lying to her mother and sneaking around behind her back. A better solution, Beck says, would have been for the mother to tell her daughter that she understood that the drill team was important to her, and she could re-join as soon as her grades came up, whether at the end of next week, next month, or next grading period.

Let natural consequences occur. Don't nag your children—or rescue them. If your daughter leaves her wet bathing suit and towel on the bathroom floor after swim practice, let her find—and wear—the wet and smelly suit the next day.

Practice patience. We all lose it once in a while, but that doesn't mean we should give up. Unless a child's behavior is life threatening, there is always time to take a deep breath and wait for a sense of inner calm, says Aletha Solter, Ph.D., a developmental psychologist who runs the Aware Parenting Institute in Goleta, California, a program that helps parents of young children improve their parenting skills.

Step back and purposefully delay discussion, suggests Dr. Kersey. When you feel like you're losing it, tell your child that you are too upset to deal with the problem now, and you want him to come back in 10 minutes—or 1 hour, or at 7 tonight—and talk about it then. This gives you time to cool off and your child time to think about the possible consequences, to reassess his actions, and to think about what he might have done differently or what he might do next time.

Another suggestion: put another face on your child. Pretend she's a friend. How would you talk to her? Chances are you'd be more careful, more patient, and kinder, she says. Remember, you're always modeling how to live.

The corollary to this rule: Pick your battles. In the heat of an argument, logic and reason fly out the window, and before you know it, you're screaming about things that don't really matter.

Say you're sorry. Apologizing makes everyone feel better and teaches your child how to apologize. "I can't apologize for my feelings, but if they have been expressed inappropriately, I must say that I am sorry for that," Antony says. Take it a step further and ask for forgiveness. That requires the child to think about accepting

your apology and to verbalize acceptance of it.

Find a system. Ann Burrows of Norfolk, Virginia, for instance, uses a system of privilege tickets with her 10-year-old daughter, Morgan. If Morgan behaves well in a particular situation, she earns the tickets, which can be redeemed for special treats or outings.

Antony keeps a family calendar. Her rule is "If you don't write it down, I don't know about it, and I'm free to schedule you for something else." Each of her daughters has an assignment pad with a calendar for tracking her own homework, projects, and other commitments.

Hold family meetings. They're a good forum for calmly discussing everyone's problems and concerns.

Follow the 50/50 rule. To counteract the generally negative attitude of teens, make sure conversations with them are at least 50 percent positive or neutral, Beck says. No more than half of the conversation should focus on limit setting, rule reinforcement, or criticism. If all the talk is negative, it destroys a child's self-esteem, she says.

Know thine enemy. Be knowledgeable about the signs and symptoms of drug and alcohol use, Beck says. Some of the most common include bloodshot eyes, slurred speech, poor motor skills, memory loss, and lethargy. Other signs include disappearance of money from the home, deterioration in family relationships and academic performance, and withdrawal from extracurricular activities. Provide a healthy atmosphere for alternative activities. She recommends consciously deciding on a mix of family activities and independent time for teens so the children maintain a healthy respect for the family unit.

Consider the source. Sometimes anger at our children stems from our own youth. We feel angry when they do something that *we* were punished for or that *we* feel guilty about from our childhood. Making these connections allows us to see the situation with less anger and intensity, to feel more compassionate toward our children, and to come up with creative solutions to conflicts, Dr. Solter says.

These are some signs that your anger may stem from your own past.

- You feel an urge to harm your child.
- Your child's behavior doesn't interfere with any present, legitimate need of your own (for example, the child's room is messy), yet you still get furious.
- Your spouse is not as disturbed by the child's behavior as you are.
- You've had similar, underlying feelings in other relationships, such as a feeling of powerlessness.

Get help. A stressed-out mother is justified in seeking as much help and support as she can find to keep herself and her family in shape, Dr. Solter says. Support can come from many sources—friends, extended family, a support group or religious community, schools, a therapist or counselor, social agencies, children's activity groups, or even a book or class on parenting or stress reduction.

Dr. Kersey recommends seeking advice from people who love you or your child, such as parents, siblings, grandparents, and other relatives. Or ask someone whose children you like and admire.

Get over the guilt. Good parenting skills—spending time with our children, listening attentively, and encouraging their efforts—are more crucial to successful development of our children than the state of our house or bank account.

ON THE FRONT LINES
A Day Care Teacher

Each weekday morning before the sun is fully up, Sharon Parker is at Children's Harbor day care center in Norfolk, Virginia, awaiting the arrival of nearly three dozen sometimes boisterous, sometimes teary 2-year-olds who will be under her watch for the next 8 hours.

While some of us might find such a day more stressful than an IRS tax audit, Parker loves it. "There's nothing more precious than a child," she says. "They're our greatest resource, and that's the way I treat them."

Loving and nurturing children comes naturally to this 46-year-old because she's always been surrounded by family, all of whom loved and supported her. She still lives in the middle-class neighborhood in which she grew up the second of six children. She credits family and faith with enabling her to work with children while raising her own son as a single parent.

In caring for children, clear communication is essential, she says. If a child is crying in the morning, for instance, Parker talks to the toddler and acknowledges her feelings. "I say, 'I know you're sad, and you don't want your mama to leave, and you're going to miss her, but she'll come back. I'm glad you're here with me. Aren't you glad to be here with your friends?' "

She tells Mom to call and check in later. Usually the child is calm by then, so Parker can reassure Mom and get her input. Is there anything that might be bothering the child—a bad night's sleep, a busy weekend, a loss or illness in the family?

When a child misbehaves, Parker gets down on the child's level to talk. "I use words that command, such as 'You will not hit the other children.' I say it twice to be sure they understand." She prefers redirecting behavior to putting a child in time-out. She'll take the toddler to a different play area, watch for a few minutes, and then praise good behavior: "I like it when you play with your friends. You're sharing the bowl—that's nice."

"Children are so cute and so helpless and so defenseless," Parker says. "All they need is a smile and a kind word. When you try to take away their rights or get in a power struggle, you bring on stress."

The Eighth Circle: The Workplace

While nearly half of American workers suffer from symptoms of burnout, a disabling reaction to stress on the job, employed women report nearly twice men's level of stress-related illness and a higher likelihood of burning out, says Naomi Swanson, Ph.D., chief of the work organization and stress research section for the National Institute of Occupational Safety and Health in Cincinnati.

The reasons for the differences are still under study, she says, because so much past research on work stress focused on men. As a result, sex-specific work stressors—including various forms of sex discrimination and difficulties combining work and family—have received little attention.

But it's there, she says. "In terms of hiring and promotion differences, sex discrimination is pervasive. Barriers to advancement to higher managerial positions are widespread, with 60 percent of women in one survey reporting that they had little or no opportunity for advancement." Also, she adds, barriers to financial and career advancement—common frustrations of female employees—have been linked to more frequent physical and psychological symptoms of stress and to more frequent visits to the doctor.

Overall, stress is caused when our jobs don't meet our expectations. Most of us try to fix the mismatch by changing how *we* respond to stressful situations at work. And that's a start. But research has shown that to avoid burning out in today's demanding workplace, we also need to take steps to alleviate stress at its source—our jobs.

The Changing Workplace

Conventional wisdom blames job stress on the individual, pinning burnout on character flaws, behavior, or productivity. According to this viewpoint, people are the problem, and the solution is to change them, says Christina Maslach, Ph.D., professor of psychology at the University of California, Berkeley.

But research shows otherwise. Over the past 20 years, Dr. Maslach has interviewed thousands of workers in dozens of occupations across North America to understand their feelings about work. What she's found is that burnout, and the chronic stress that causes it, is a problem not of individuals but of the places in which they work.

"The workplace today is a cold, hostile, demanding environment, both economically and psychologically," says Dr. Maslach, coauthor of *The Truth about Burnout: How Organizations Cause Personal Stress and What You Can Do about It.*

In their quest to adapt to a 24/7 global economy, companies everywhere are downsizing, outsourcing, and restructuring, leaving employees at all levels feeling stressed, insecure, frustrated, and alienated. The stresses and strains of all this organizational change then take root in the minds and bodies of the employees who have to adapt to it, resulting in physical and psychological stress, she says. Consider these findings from the American Institute for Stress in New York City.

- On an average workday, an estimated 1 million workers are absent because of stress-related complaints.
- Stress is thought to be responsible for more than half of the 550 million workdays lost annually because of absenteeism.
- A 3-year study conducted by a large corporation showed that 60 percent of employee absences were due to psychological problems, such as stress.

A seeming contradiction in the wake of the ever-increasing incidence of stress-related illness is the fact that for women, employment seems to be associated with better health. That may be due to what experts call the healthy worker effect—it's easier for healthy women to get and keep jobs than it is for women in poorer health, speculates Dr. Swanson.

SAVE YOUR HEART: LEAVE YOUR BAD DAY AT THE OFFICE

Just because your workday ends and it's time to head home doesn't mean your mind is off the job. And that can have an impact on your health.

Dutch researchers found that job overcommitment—feeling competitive, impatient, obsessed, or unable to let go—may increase heart disease risk by reducing your body's ability to dissolve blood clots.

These findings could be an important clue to understanding—and reversing—the effect that job stress has on cardiovascular health, says Tanja G. M. Vrijkotte, a researcher in the department of biological psychology at Vrije University in Amsterdam and the lead author on the Dutch study. In addition to possible clotting problems, those who scored high on overcommitment were also at risk for feelings of exhaustion and physiological breakdown, she says.

Though researchers haven't yet determined which treatments can best defuse overcommitment, taking time to destress during the work week could help.

And when you come home, check your briefcase at the door.

"The fact is that work benefits women by increasing our possibilities for economic independence, higher self-esteem, and social support. Women often work because they want to, not because they have to," she says. Given that, it pays to find a job—and work environment—that keeps you emotionally and physically healthy.

When Your Job No Longer Fits

When there is a mismatch between the nature of the job and the nature of the person, the result is stress. Ignore that stress and you're at greater risk for developing burnout, a condition marked by feelings of exhaustion, cynicism, and ineffectiveness.

Dr. Maslach calls it the "erosion of the soul." You lose your motivation for work. Tasks that you used to enjoy become sheer drudgery. Many people generalize their stress by simply complaining about overwork. But researchers have actually identified six key areas where our personalities need to match with our jobs: workload, control, reward, community, fairness, and values. The better the match, the more likely you are to be happy in your work and avoid job burnout.

Workload. When you have to do too much in too little time with too few resources, you feel overwhelmed and stretched beyond capacity. "Work overload is perhaps the most obvious indication of a mismatch between the person and the job," says Dr. Maslach. "People are working longer hours but are still not able to keep up with overwhelming demands." Indeed, a recent AFL-CIO survey of 765 working women found that 60 percent worked more than 40 hours per week. We arrive for breakfast meetings, munch through lunch at our desks, and then log on to the computer at home to prepare for the next day.

Lack of control. Rigid policies, micromanaging, or a chaotic work environment prevent you from making choices about your work and following through on your projects. "This kind of monitoring sends the message 'You can't be trusted, we don't respect your judgment, you're incapable of doing this by yourself,'" explains Dr. Maslach.

Reward. Maybe your pay is the pits, or your supervisor never utters a word of praise. When you don't get recognition, it feels like your work isn't valued. With today's tight budgets and

overtaxed management, generous pay raises are a thing of the past and salary freezes the norm. "What's most devastating is the loss of internal reward that comes when a person takes pride in doing something of value to others, and does that job well," says Dr. Maslach.

Community. Women function best when they share a positive connection with others in the workplace, says Dr. Maslach. We thrive on

AM I BURNING OUT?

Beverly Potter, Ph.D., a psychologist in Berkeley, California, and author of *Overcoming Job Burnout: How to Renew Enthusiasm for Work*, likens burned-out workers to the Greek mythological character Sisyphus, who was condemned for eternity to roll a boulder up a hill, only to have it tumble back down just before reaching the top. A leading authority on the causes and prevention of burnout, Dr. Potter developed this quiz to help workers assess their own risk of burning out. Read each of the following statements and rate how often each is true for you.

Rarely true   1   2   3   4   5   Usually true

1. I feel tired even when I've gotten adequate sleep. _____
2. I am dissatisfied with my work. _____
3. I feel sad for no apparent reason. _____
4. I am forgetful. _____
5. I am irritable and snap at people. _____
6. I avoid people at work and in my private life. _____
7. I have trouble sleeping due to worry about work. _____
8. I get sick more than I used to. _____
9. My attitude about work is "Why bother?" _____
10. I often get into conflicts. _____
11. My job performance is not up to par. _____

12. I use alcohol and/or drugs to feel better. _____

13. Communicating with others is a strain. _____

14. I can't concentrate on my work like I once could. _____

15. I am easily bored with my work. _____

16. I work hard but accomplish little. _____

17. I feel frustrated with my work. _____

18. I don't like going to work. _____

19. Social activities are draining. _____

20. Sex is not worth the effort. _____

21. I watch TV most of the time when not working. _____

22. I don't have much to look forward to in my work. _____

23. I worry about work during my off hours. _____

24. Feelings about work interfere with my personal life. _____

25. My work seems pointless. _____

   Scoring: Add up your responses and check the following key to rate your burnout.
   25 to 50. You're doing well.
   51 to 75. You're okay if you take preventive action.
   76 to 100. You're a candidate for burnout.
   101 to 125. You're burning out.

the praise, comfort, happiness, and humor that we share with others. But often our jobs isolate us physically and socially. We may spend all day focused on a computer screen or simply be too busy to get together with coworkers. Most destructive is chronic and unresolved conflict. Tensions with others on the job make you feel frustrated, angry, fearful, and suspicious. "Conflict tears apart the fabric of social support,

making it less likely that people will help each other out when the going gets tough," says Dr. Maslach.

Fairness. Does your office load the work on some, while others reap the rewards? Are certain people more likely to have their grievances heard, while others are ignored? When you think you haven't been treated fairly, you end up feeling distrustful, disloyal, and cynical.

Values. When your job requires you to behave unethically or do things that clash with your own personal values, you're caught in a conflict. Honor yourself or keep your job? Lie to that client in order to make the sale, or forgo the commission? In either case, you end up feeling bad, either about yourself or about the job.

Redesign Your Job

Nearly half of all large companies in the United States provide some type of stress-management training for workers. These programs teach workers about the nature and sources of stress, the effects of stress on health, and personal skills, such as time management or relaxation exercises, to reduce stress. Some companies also provide individual counseling for employees with work and personal problems. Yet stress-management techniques that focus on the individual are only temporary fixes because they're not addressing the cause of the stress—your work environment, says Dr. Maslach. The solution is to address both the person and the workplace.

"People are not powerless in the workplace. Even on a small level, there are changes we can make that will help," says Dr. Swanson. Studies show that employees who actively address prob-

HELP FROM EMPLOYERS

Most employers are willing to offer flexibility and other perks in order to make life a little easier for their employees.

"Employers know that in order to remain competitive, they need to offer benefits that help employees balance their work and personal lives," says Carol Sladek, work/life consultant for Hewitt Associates, a global management consulting firm based in Lincolnshire, Illinois.

It its 1999 work/life survey of 1,020 major U.S. companies—including 85 percent of the Fortune 100 and 57 percent of the Fortune 500 companies—Hewitt found companies offering the following benefits.

Flexible scheduling arrangements. Seventy-four percent of the companies surveyed offered flexible work schedules, up from 66 percent in 1994. Typical options included flextime (57 percent), part-time employment (47 percent), job sharing (28 percent), telecommuting (28 percent), compressed work schedules (20 percent), and summer hours (12 percent).

Child care assistance. Overall, 90 percent of employers offered some type of child care benefits to employees. Four out of five employers offered dependent care spending accounts to provide tax breaks to eligible employees. Other child care benefits included resource and referral services (42 percent), sick or emergency child care programs (13 percent) and on-site or near-site child care centers (10 percent).

Elder care programs. Elder care programs continue to grow in popularity, with 47 percent of employers surveyed providing assistance, up from 40 percent in 1998 and 24 percent in 1994.

Of elder care programs offered, dependent care spending accounts (32 percent), resources and referral services (40 percent), long-term care insurance (17 percent), and counseling (4 percent) were the most prominent.

On-site personal services. Just over half of employers provided some type of on-site convenience or personal services to employees, such as ATMs (34 percent) and banking services (22 percent), travel services (18 percent), dry cleaning (15 percent), and discount purchases (12 percent).

Casual dress. Nearly two-thirds (60 percent) of employers offered casual or business casual dress. Thirty-five percent offered full-time casual dress, while 19 percent offered casual dress on Fridays.

Financial security. Thirty-seven percent of surveyed employers provided financial security programs to help employees make decisions about their retirement and investments. Programs included financial planning (17 percent) and scholarships (15 percent).

Personal and professional growth. Three-fourths (75 percent) of surveyed employers provided educational assistance and personal and professional growth programs. Opportunities included educational reimbursement (74 percent), on- and off-site developmental seminars or workshops (24 percent), and career counseling (4 percent).

Family and medical leave. Twelve percent offered more than the 12 weeks' leave required by the Family and Medical Leave Act of 1993. Seventy-five percent provided the minimum 12 weeks.

lems in the workplace report less burnout than those who take a more passive approach.

Here's how to help turn your workplace into a more humane environment.

Take the lead. You can't turn the workplace around all by yourself, but you can jump-start the process by taking on a leadership role. First pinpoint the ways that your job stresses you out, advises Dr. Swanson.

Studies show that different occupations typically generate different types of stressors. For clerical workers, it's lack of control. For nurses, it's conflict with coworkers, while female assembly line workers and sewing machine operators link high workloads with job dissatisfaction and stress.

Connect with coworkers. "To make an impact, you'll need to make it a group project," explains Dr. Maslach. Meet with coworkers to share concerns, but don't use the meeting as a gripe session. Instead, use the time to come up with realistic solutions. Then get the group to agree on one problem to address first. Usually it's the one with the highest burnout potential and the potential for concrete solutions. Because the six areas described above are interrelated, improvement in one area tends to improve others.

Take it to the next level. You and your group have come up with some great ideas. "Your solutions cannot be implemented in a vacuum; they have to be implemented within

DE-STRESSING WITH DESKTOP YOGA

An increasing amount of research shows an association between job stress and neck, shoulder, and lower-back pain, and repetitive stress injuries like carpal tunnel syndrome, especially among women. Though they're not sure why, researchers speculate it may be because women's jobs are more likely to be stressful, monotonous, and repetitive than men's.

"The most important thing is to get up from your desk and move around every half-hour," says Ellen Serber, a certified Iyengar yoga instructor who has been teaching the San Francisco Bay area since 1978. And try the following stretches, or "desktop yoga." Remember while you're doing a stretch to relax your belly and breathe slowly and deeply. "A slow, long exhale is calming," explains Serber.

These exercises stimulate blood circulation, relax eyestrain, and warm and stretch muscles made tense and rigid by static work positions.

Extended full-body stretch. Stand with your feet hip-width apart and your arms at your sides. With palms facing down, raise your arms to shoulder level. Extend your fingers and stretch through the elbows. As you exhale, rotate your shoulders back and turn your palms up. On your next exhale, bring your arms overhead with the palms facing each other. Press your feet into the floor to stretch your torso. After a few breaths, interlock your fingers and press your palms up toward the ceiling, stretching open your fingers and palms. Hold this stretch, and then, on an exhale, bend your body to the side. Repeat the complete stretch on the other side. You can also do this stretch seated at your desk. Make sure you press your thighs deeply into your chair as you stretch up.

Releasing your neck. Shrug your shoulders high up to your ears and then release and drop. Repeat at least three times.

Shaking out the tension. Shake out your wrists and arms, letting them dangle from your shoulders. Rotate your shoulders forward and back.

Relaxing your eyes and breathing. Turn your head right and left, focusing your eyes into the far distance. Close your eyes and take three deep slow breaths.

the organization," says Dr. Maslach. "The crucial step is to gather support for your cause." Employers' solutions tend to focus only on how to change the workload. But better solutions should also address the five other areas of mismatch between worker and workplace. Get the ball rolling by drafting a proposal of your group's solutions and presenting it to management.

Emphasize the process. You may come up with a solution to one problem, then hit a snag 3 months down the road. Work is always evolving, so the problem-solving process is actually more important than reaching a "happily ever after" ending, says Dr. Maslach. The other half of the equation is to sharpen your own self-management skills so you feel more in control and stress resilient. "Just setting attainable goals can increase your sense of control," says Beverly Potter, Ph.D., a psychologist in Berkeley, California, and author of *Overcoming Job Burnout: How to Renew Enthusiasm for Work.*

Improve your own marketability. Network within your company, call a local community college, or hire a tutor to increase your skills. Learning new skills provides you with a sense of control and the confidence necessary to tackle new challenges and handle the unexpected. Skill building also helps reduce stress by making you feel more in control.

Work less. There is a perceived social norm that it's wimpy to leave work before the cleaning staff comes in, says Dr. Maslach. But new research suggests that grueling hours are no longer a prerequisite for success: More than one-third of employees who choose to work reduced hours *are* promoted, according to a study. In the study, managers were able to reduce their hours by one-third without losing their effectiveness. The key to a successful reduced-hours work arrangement: a supportive boss. The study found that 70 percent of supervisors supported employees who wanted to work fewer hours.

Get by with a little help from your friends. People on the road to job burnout tend to have no life outside of work. "When you're isolated, you feel weak and vulnerable," says Dr. Potter. Share your problems with friends, or join a professional association.

Take a nap. You're more apt to feel stressed by little things when you're tired. Most people have a dip in energy levels sometime between 1:00 and 3:00 P.M. Your attention wanders, you make more mistakes, and you're more likely to say something you may regret. That's the perfect time for a siesta, advises Camille Anthony, president of the Napping Company in Reading, Massachusetts, and coauthor of *The Art of Napping at Work.* An afternoon nap of 30 minutes or less can elevate your mood, restore energy, and improve how you relate to coworkers.

Despite the beneficial effects of naps, however, most companies aren't setting up nap areas. If you drive to work, use your car as a nap spot (as long as you're parked in a safe location). For women, the most popular place to nap is on a chair or couch in the rest room, Anthony says.

Learn to detach. For some workers, it's almost impossible not to burn out: the social worker with the 100-person caseload, or the oncology nurse. That's when you need to develop what Dr. Potter calls "detached concern," focusing on your efforts and letting go of the results. "When Mother Teresa was asked how she could stand to work with sick and dying children, she is reported to have said, 'I love them while they are here.' Her love was the concern, and the 'while they are here' was her detachment," he says.

Call it quits. Sometimes, the best solution is to change jobs, says Dr. Potter. However, if the burned-out employee quits without analyzing the source of dissatisfaction and grabs the next job that comes along, the new job can be just as bad. Before you quit, know what you need in a job and how to go out and get it.

The Ninth Circle:
The 21st Century

In 1995, 168 people were killed and hundreds injured in the terrorist bombing of the Oklahoma City federal building. In 1997, the world was stunned by news that 36-year-old Diana, Princess of Wales, had been killed in a freakish car wreck. In 1999, 12 students and a teacher were killed by two gun-toting students at Columbine High School in Colorado. And a year later, 17 sailors aboard the USS *Cole* died in a terrorist attack during a refueling stop in Yemen.

As if that weren't enough, vivid images of floods, earthquakes, famine, horrific airplane crashes, child abuse, and wars emanate in a seemingly endless stream from our televisions, newspapers, magazines, radios, and computer screens.

"We can't avoid it," says Pamela Peeke, M.D., assistant clinical professor of medicine at the University of Maryland in Baltimore and author of *Fight Fat after Forty*.

Most of us have enough stress in our own homes—raising children, maintaining marriages, holding down careers, keeping house. So when we're constantly bombarded by additional external stress, it can be overwhelming, says Shelley Neiderbach, Ph.D., a psychotherapist and certified trauma specialist and executive director of Crime Victims' Counseling Services in Brooklyn, New York.

But we can learn to keep it in perspective. We can cope while remaining informed, and even find ways to contribute in our own small way.

Learning "Self-Talk"

"There's nothing inherently upsetting or distressing about negative news, whether it's politics or crime," says Walt Schafer, Ph.D., professor of sociology at California State University at Chico and author of *Stress Management for Wellness*. "It depends on what you make of it."

We can react by tuning out or becoming angry or cynical. Or we can mobilize our concern by reaching out and contributing to the common good.

Dr. Schafer, for example, began donating to an orphanage in Kenya after he visited the African country when his daughter served there in the Peace Corps. He was moved by the strong need: Kenya has a high birth rate and a stagnant economy, so most children there receive little education.

He now teaches his students about the conditions there and has convinced his local Rotary Club to donate $3,000 to help build a school at the orphanage.

"It's not a great deal, but it's what I can do—and it's very meaningful to me in my small way," Dr. Schafer says.

It also provides him with some sense of control over events he can't eradicate alone, he says.

"When you feel the worst about something is when you feel like you can't control it," says Dr. Peeke. And while we can't control world events, we can control our perspective.

"Bring it back down to you," says Dr. Peeke. "Say: 'Maybe I can call that hospital and volunteer. Maybe I will touch another human life. And even if it's just one life, then maybe I've made a difference.'"

Leslie VanSant, a spokeswoman for the American Red Cross in Washington, D.C., remembers a young boy who donated his entire allowance—$40—when he heard about the summer fires that ravaged Montana in 2000.

Whether it's in time or dollars, says VanSant, many people find that giving "is good for the soul."

Avoiding Overload

Still, the reality is that we can't be everything to everyone.

ON THE FRONT LINES
An Air Traffic Manager

As air traffic manager of New York TRACON, or Terminal Radar Approach Control, in Westbury, New York, Loretta Martin, 48, is on call 24 hours a day, 7 days a week, managing 300 Federal Aviation Administration (FAA) employees, including about 250 air traffic controllers at about 50 airports along the East Coast. Some of the nation's largest airports—La Guardia and Kennedy in New York, and Newark in New Jersey—are among them.

Martin, in essence, oversees all that goes on in the air from the time an aircraft takes off until it is cleared for landing. She works with both commercial airlines and the military whose airspace is in her region.

And she is responsible for a multitude of duties from her Long Island office, such as approving the installation of new radar equipment and dealing with politicians, labor unions, budgets, delays, and even communities on noise issues.

A former commercial airline pilot and air traffic controller herself, Martin has been air traffic manager since 1994. "I didn't find the flying stressful at all, and I didn't find controlling traffic stressful at all," Martin says. "But I do find the position I'm in now creates some anxiety or stress just because of the tremendous responsibility involved and all the different avenues I have to be on top of."

When TWA Flight 800 exploded over the Atlantic in 1996, killing all aboard, Martin received a call at her Long Island home. She was told that controllers had lost contact with the aircraft off Kennedy Airport. Martin hopped into

Try to do that, and it's a sure ticket to the helplessness and hopelessness that are the hallmarks of toxic, health-robbing stress, says Dr. Peeke.

One answer: Limit your exposure to the media.

her car for the 45-minute trek to Kennedy, where she spent the next 24 hours reviewing files on the aircraft and the performance of the controllers and listening to the voice tape. Such information is then passed along for review at FAA headquarters in Washington, D.C.

Some days are so busy, she forgets to eat lunch. But Martin makes time to relax. "It would be very difficult, I think, if you didn't have some kind of an outlet to deal with this kind of stress," she says.

Near her home and office, she keeps two horses and tries to ride daily for about 45 minutes. The horses are jumpers, which means that she must focus to avoid mistakes and injury.

It's extremely de-stressing, she says. "I have to concentrate on several things, especially if I'm jumping, so it totally takes my mind off these other issues." Unlike an airplane, she says, a horse has a mind of its own. "It really kind of entraps your focus."

She and her husband, Michael, also enjoy riding motorcycles together. When the couple met, more than 7 years ago, Martin rode on the back of Michael's cycle. Now she owns a Harley Low Rider. The bike weighs more than 1,000 pounds, while Martin carries about 135 pounds on her 5'11" frame. Focus, again, is the key to her safety and stress relief, she says.

In the mornings before readying herself for work, Martin also practices a series of yoga movements she learned more than a decade ago. "It makes me feel physically better," she says of those 10 minutes. "I also like my vegetable state—every once in a while, to sit like a couch potato."

Shelley Neiderbach, Ph.D., a psychotherapist and executive director of Crime Victims' Counseling Services in Brooklyn, New York, recommends taking a "media vacation" of at least a week when you feel overwhelmed.

"When you turn on your television or listen to your car radio, you get not one account a day of the latest atrocity, but you get it 50 times a day. That can pretty much numb you out," she explains.

We become "witnesses" to the crime or tragedy in an unacknowledged, unconscious way. "We don't realize we're being traumatized by it," Dr. Neiderbach says. "We think we're just watching the news."

When we unplug from this media overload, she says, "it's kind of like taking a bath when you're dirty. You wash away the effects of continuous exposure and you feel better."

Too much of a news junkie to turn it off? Dr. Peeke suggests choosing one newspaper or television forecast a day. "And absolutely infuse your day with stress-resilient moments," she says. Take a walk outdoors, call a friend, offer to help an elderly person with errands.

And choose wisely. Most of us seldom stop to think about what we're viewing, says W. James Potter, Ph.D., visiting professor of communications at UCLA and author of *Media Literacy*.

"Most people's minds are just on default," he says. "They float along and the media happens to them, rather than their getting control of all the messages the media is putting in their minds."

He suggests that we tune in to our feelings and our goals and monitor what's going on inside us as we listen, so we don't become desensitized or jaded—not only to news in the world but to suffering in our own communities and families.

Here, then, are some strategies for coping

with information overload, when we feel tense, anxious—and when we've simply had enough.

Set an example. Limit your television and video viewing. Violence and tragedy not only are part of the news but also occur in sitcoms, dramas, cartoons, and video games. Monitor what your children watch and listen to. The American Medical Association (AMA) suggests turning on the television only when there is something specific that you want to watch, not simply to see what's on.

Watch reel life. Learn about movies at local theaters. Be clear with your children about your guidelines for appropriate viewing, and talk to them about their choices. And don't be embarrassed to walk away if you don't like what you see. In a survey by the American Medical Association, two-thirds of adults and 75 percent of those with children walked out of a movie because the content was too violent.

Mind your moves. Walk, skate, bicycle, dance. By focusing on your movement, you take a mental break from the world at large. And you're giving yourself "a tiny squirt of beta-endorphins, the most powerful inhibitor of the stress response," says Dr. Peeke. The world may not be at peace, but you likely will be.

Seek solitude. We all benefit from quiet time every now and then. "Only you can give it to yourself," says Dr. Neiderbach. Try commuting to work in silence. At the office, steer clear of water cooler talk about the latest world events. Walk down the hall; take an elevator

---

WOMAN TO WOMAN
She Can Hardly Watch the News

Gwendolyn, a 52-year-old schoolteacher in Virginia Beach, sometimes gets so upset by certain news stories on her television or in print that she feels a kind of "blind rage" within. She wants to stay informed, however. So she's learned to tune out bad news without turning her back on the world or her community. This is her story.

I was dressing for work one morning not long ago when I heard a television news report that so horrified me I put my hand over my mouth to muffle my scream.

It was about a pet shelter where some dogs had been so abused that people were unlikely to adopt them because the animals looked and behaved so badly. Although the story didn't say so, I assumed the dogs would be euthanized.

I'm a pet lover with three cats. Over the years, I've taken in strays who needed love and care. I can't understand how some people can be so cruel.

That news report upset me so badly, I shook as I drove to school that day. There I talked to a coworker and fellow pet lover—a shoulder to lean on—before teaching my first class. Sharing my outrage helped calm me.

This wasn't the first time I've been visibly shaken by television or print news. Certain topics—child abuse, spousal abuse, people mistreating animals, and situations of extreme injustice, such as wars in foreign countries where people can't get food—make me angry, upset.

---

ride to nowhere. Better yet, buy some soft foam earplugs, and use them.

Be realistic. Often, we're troubled by a sense that life isn't fair. Children shouldn't die. Women shouldn't be raped. "The bottom line is, it happens," says Dr. Peeke. "And you cannot control it. The greatest stress of life comes from unmet expectations. What do you expect it to

I don't know why. I've never been a victim of domestic abuse or crime.

I talked to a therapist because I worried that my reactions were too intense. She helped me understand that I am sensitive and caring, although perhaps overly so at times. I've never wanted to take out my anger on anyone, although I do think people who abuse or victimize others should be jailed.

I take an antidepressant medication now, and, along with talk therapy, it's helped even out my emotions. Still, I know I will always be bothered by that kind of news.

As a teacher and citizen, I don't want to simply tune out. I feel a duty to be informed, so I watch television news as often as three times a day and read a daily newspaper.

Now, though, if I hear "promos" to reports about topics I think will upset me, I turn down the volume. In the newspaper, I don't read those kinds of stories.

When major tragedies happen, such as Princess Diana's death in 1997 and John Kennedy Jr.'s fatal plane crash 2 years later, I don't plunk down in front of the television and feast on unceasing, detailed reports. I think that's emotionally harmful.

I also stay away from overtly violent films, "dark" comedies—which I don't find funny—and television shows that dwell on evil or gore.

One thing I wonder about violence in the news: If there's this much on TV, how much is really out there? That scares me.

be, all happy out there? You have to make your expectations realistic. Life is tough."

Carry protection. Studies show that exposure to depictions of violence creates a climate of fear. We needn't be paralyzed by what we see, but a healthful dose of caution may be called for, says Dr. Neiderbach. Forget the handgun. One survey showed that for every time a woman used a handgun to kill in self-defense, 239 women were murdered by someone who used a handgun on them. Mace and pepper spray can turn on us with the wind. So for safety, carry a small squeeze bottle filled with soap or bleach. When you're out alone or feel threatened, carry it in your hand—not in your purse.

Look to the future. If you don't have time or energy to give now, consider making it a goal to help later—after you retire or your children go off to college, says Dr. Peeke. One woman who was suddenly widowed in her sixties joined a volunteer program to mentor troubled youths. After training, the retired secretary spent 9 months several states away from her home, living with and teaching teens—unlike anything she'd ever done. She brought home photos, videos, stories, and a sense of having made a difference.

Read for fun. Instead of scouring a newspaper or political magazine, read something escapist, "particularly novels of no consequence," says Dr. Neiderbach. "There are no commercials, and you can put it down anytime. Distraction is often just what we need for a while."

PART FOUR

Finding the Calm

The Power of Positive Thinking

Consider that it's not quite a compliment to be called a Pollyanna. The little orphan girl who brimmed with boundless cheer has come to epitomize the cockeyed optimist who doesn't quite see reality for what it is.

The fact is, positive thinking has gotten a bit of a bum rap. We tend to trivialize positive emotions like hope, joy, and contentment.

"People think they're goofing off or wasting their time when they're experiencing positive emotions," explains Barbara Fredrickson, Ph.D., associate professor of psychology at the University of Michigan in Ann Arbor. "The possible benefits of positive emotions seem undervalued in cultures like ours, which endorse the Protestant ethic and cast hard work and self-discipline as virtues, and leisure and pleasures as sinful."

But, research shows, feeling good *is* good. And if we want to find our way to natural calm, we need to nurture what is best in ourselves.

Why Be Positive?

Before World War II, psychology had three missions: curing mental illness, making the lives of people more fulfilling, and identifying and nurturing people who were gifted.

After the war, however, things changed, and the primary way for psychologists to make a living became treating people who were dysfunctional, people who had serious emotional and mental illnesses.

"But sadly, while plumbing the depths of what is worst in life, psychology lost its connection to the positive side of life—the knowledge about what makes human life most worth living, most fulfilling, most enjoyable, and most productive," says Martin E. P. Seligman, Ph.D., professor of psychology at the University of Pennsylvania in Philadelphia and founder of the positive psychology movement.

Positive psychology shifts the focus from what's *wrong* with us to what's *right* with us. The latest research in this fledgling field has shown that cultivating emotions such as optimism, joy, contentment, and interest can help prevent and treat problems—such as anxiety, depression, and stress-related health problems—rooted in negative emotions.

Need some convincing? Read on.

HOW OPTIMISTIC ARE YOU?

Do you tend to look at the bright side, or is your outlook on life more like Eeyore's, the dismal donkey from *Winnie the Pooh*? The quiz below was developed by psychologists from Carnegie Mellon University in Pittsburgh and the University of Miami in Florida to assess your tendency to be optimistic or pessimistic.

Be as honest and accurate as you can. Answer according to your own feelings, rather than how you think most people would answer. Try not to let your response to one statement influence your responses to other statements. There are no correct or incorrect answers. For each question select one of the following answers.

A. Strongly agree   D. Disagree
B. Agree   E. Strongly Disagree
C. Neutral

1. In uncertain times, I usually expect the best. ____

2. It's easy for me to relax. ____

3. If something can go wrong for me, it will. ____

4. I'm always optimistic about my future. ____

5. I enjoy my friends a lot. ____

6. It's important for me to keep busy. ____

7. I hardly ever expect things to go my way. ____

8. I don't get upset too easily. ____

9. I rarely count on good things happening to me. ____

10. Overall, I expect more good things to happen to me than bad. ____

Scoring: After you've answered all the questions, score yourself by adding up your total points.

Questions 1, 4, 10: A = 4 points, B = 3 points, C = 2 points, D = 1 point, and E = 0 point

Questions 3, 7, 9: A = 0 point, B = 1 point, C = 2 points, D = 3 points, and E = 4 points

Questions 2, 5, 6, 8: These questions don't really count. No score.

0 to 10 points: Pessimist. Your outlook on the future is pretty bleak. You don't adjust well to life's transitions. Rather than face problems head-on, you tend to deny that there is a problem. And when faced with stress, you're more likely to give up on your goals.

11 to 17 points: Realist. You're neither highly optimistic nor highly pessimistic. Research shows that most people typically score in the 14- to 15-point range.

18 to 24 points: Optimist. You tend to have positive expectations for the future. You're more likely to accept life's problems and cope with challenges. And when you can't solve a problem, you lighten up with a dash of humor. You look for the positive in every situation.

Positive people are stress resilient. When Susan Folkman, Ph.D., professor of medicine and codirector of the Center for AIDS Prevention Studies at the University of California, San Francisco, studied AIDS caregivers who are under chronic stress, she found that those who cultivated positive emotions in their day-to-day tasks coped best with stress. They were more optimistic, felt more in control, and adapted better to stressful situations. "Positive emotions may serve as a buffer against some of the adverse physiological consequences of stress," she says.

Positive people are better problem solvers. The more positive you are, the more flexible and constructive your coping skills are, explains Lisa Aspinwall, Ph.D., associate professor of psychology at the University of Utah in Salt Lake City. "Optimists are less likely to avoid their problems," she says. They're more likely to seek active solutions, to view a problem as a challenge instead of a threat, to ask for advice, or to seek the support of friends. And that can help them avoid depression, she says, since "avoidance coping," when you ignore problems or uncomfortable situations—a typical behavior of negative thinkers—is a big risk factor for depression.

Positive people take better care of their health. Ever read an article about the health risks of caffeine, smoking, or obesity and then put it out of your mind? Well, another study shows that positive thinkers are more likely to pay attention to health risk information that's relevant to them. Researchers at the University of Maryland asked a group of women who regularly consumed caffeine to recall an instance when they were kind. Then they gave the women health information about the link between caffeine consumption and fibrocystic breast disease. The women who had been asked to recall a kindness remembered more health risk facts and were more likely to change their behavior based on what they'd learned than those who hadn't been asked to recall a kindness.

"This shows how positive emotions spill over into other areas of our lives," says Dr. Aspinwall. "It's not a frill to feel good. It plays an important role in how we learn about ourselves and others and how we cope with stress."

Positive people are happier. Your happiness may be written all over your face. Researchers at the University of California, Berkeley, studied photos of 112 women from a 1958 yearbook. They were able to gauge levels of positive emotion (psych-speak for happiness) for each woman by noting the degree of muscle contrac-

tion in her facial expression.

"Then we wondered, 'Does that predict what her life will be like for the next 30 years?'" says Dacher Keltner, Ph.D., associate professor of psychology at the school. As it turns out, it did. When they interviewed the women 3 decades later, they found that those who had displayed the most positive emotion in their photos were less likely to feel distressed about their lives. They also were more likely to be married and to display a sense of well-being, and they generally felt happier about their lives.

Turn Your Thinking Around

So how do we learn to become a "glass half-full" type of person instead of a "glass half-empty" person? First, understand what that means.

"Positive emotions are more than the absence of negative emotions," says Dr. Fredrickson.

One of the misunderstandings about this way of thinking is that all you have to do is put on a happy face, says Dr. Keltner. But thinking positive involves taking an alternative approach, and that requires a great deal of hard work. It's difficult and taxing, he says, but ultimately rewarding.

Put on your rose-tinted glasses. Studies show that people in difficult situations who are able to reframe their circumstances in a more positive light cope with stress better. For instance, Dr. Folkman found that the AIDS caregivers who focused on the value of their efforts and commented on how their caregiving activities demonstrated their love and preserved the dignity of their ill partners fared best.

To get a rosier view of your own life, look at the lessons you've learned from a bad situation, suggests Dr. Folkman. Or simply give yourself a well-deserved pat on the back when you've just endured a very stressful situation. Say to yourself, "I didn't realize I could do that."

Act happy. We can act ourselves into a more positive frame of mind, says David G. Myers,

Ph.D., author of *The Pursuit of Happiness*. Research has shown that simply manipulating your face into a smiling expression by holding a pen in your teeth can make you feel better. On the other hand, hold the pen in your lips, and you activate the frowning muscles. "Scowl and the whole world seems to scowl back," he says.

"Going through the motions can trigger the emotions," says Dr. Myers. "So . . . put on a happy face. Talk as if you feel positive, optimistic, and outgoing," even if you don't.

Take control of your time. Happy people feel in control of their lives. But stress makes you feel as if your life is out of control. "We often overestimate how much we will accomplish in any given day, which leaves us feeling frustrated," says Dr. Myers.

When you start feeling like this, it's best to focus on immediate goals, advises Dr. Folkman. Make a to-do list for the day. Sounds pretty basic, right? Here's the difference. Make sure the tasks are specific and small, such as "Mail letter to Aunt Hilda," not "Organize my closet." The more, the better. And then (and this is key) take *pleasure* in crossing each one off as you accomplish it. "It reduces anxiety and helps you regain a sense of control because you feel more effective. And that's no small thing," she says.

Laugh it up. "Laughter is a good thing in times of stress. That's why people often laugh at unlikely times—like at a funeral, for example," explains Dr. Keltner. He interviewed mourners and noted how often they laughed and

JUST THINKING POSITIVE ISN'T ENOUGH

A familiar fantasy: You decide it's time to lose weight and resolve that you're going to eat less and exercise more. You imagine yourself 20 pounds thinner and bask in the fantasy of how great you'll look in a swimsuit next summer.

The familiar reality: You start with the best of intentions. For 3 days, everything goes as planned. But on day 4, you come home from work totally stressed out and eat your way through the refrigerator. On day 5, you give up and chalk up one more diet failure.

What went wrong? Sure, stress was a big part of the picture. But something else was, as well. New research shows that when it comes to actually changing our behavior, it's not enough to simply *think* positive.

"There are two types of thinking about the future: expectations and fantasy," says Gabrielle Oettingen, Ph.D., associate professor of psychology at New York University. She's studied our thinking processes on everything from weight loss to recovery from surgery, from improving grades to finding a job. She's found that in order to get going and stay motivated, we need a dash of negative thinking.

"You have to do more than have positive fantasies. By simply imagining yourself where you already want to be, you feel like you're already there, so why act?" she explains. "You have to mentally contrast positive fantasies with the negative aspects of reality that stand in the way."

So in the weight-loss scenario above, follow up the fantasies of the slimmed-down you with visions of some of the obstacles you'll have to overcome to get there: Sweating through more workouts, giving up your 4:00 P.M. Hershey bar, saying no to seconds.

"If you follow these steps, chances are better that you'll formulate binding goals and attain those goals," Dr. Oettingen says.

expressed positive emotion. Two years later, he interviewed them again and found that those who had displayed the most positive emotions were least likely to have experienced depression and

DE-STRESSING PLACES

A Rocking Chair

Looking for a place to unwind? Try the soothing rhythm of an old-fashioned rocking chair.

"There's a stereotype of older people on a porch happily going back and forth in their rocking chairs," says Nancy M. Watson, R.N., Ph.D., assistant professor at the University of Rochester School of Nursing in New York. "It turns out that the activity really does bring some peace of mind."

In a study of 25 nursing home residents in which aides observed residents who rocked from 30 minutes to 2½ hours a day over 6 weeks, the use of a rocking chair eased emotional distress.

Right away aides noticed a dramatic effect: Rocking in the chair seemed to calm the rocker down when he or she was emotionally upset. Behaviors like crying or expressions of anxiety, tension, and depression were less frequent in the 11 patients who rocked more than 80 minutes a day.

Those who rocked the most improved the most. They even looked happy.

Researchers are not sure why it works but speculate that rocking may stimulate the production of endorphins, calming hormones produced by the body after exercise.

"Even though we don't have scientific evidence, it makes sense to think that rocking can have similar effects on younger, healthier people, too," says Dr. Watson.

So the next time you feel stressed, head for the rocking chair.

anxiety. In times of stress, laughter reduces the physiological reaction to stress and feelings of anxiety and helps people form stronger bonds with others.

Be social. We feel better when we're interacting with others, says Dr. Myers. So give priority to close relationships. If you're married, resolve to nurture your relationship, to not take your partner for granted. Treat your husband with the same kindness that you display to others. To rejuvenate your affections, act lovingly, play together, and share common interests, he says.

Savor positive moments. We may not realize it, but even when we're under stress, we also experience positive moments. In 1,794 interviews with AIDS caregivers, Dr. Folkman was surprised to find that 99.5 percent were able to recall a positive event—something that made them feel good and helped them get through the day.

So tune in to those moments when they happen. "They give you a moment of relief—like relaxing a muscle that's been tense for a long time. That brief moment can be restorative," says Dr. Folkman.

It could be a compliment, observing a beautiful sunset, or hearing your teenager say, "Thanks, Mom." Or it could be something planned, such as a special meal or a get-together with friends.

Delight in those ordinary but positive moments in your day, and amplify them, says Dr. Folkman. For instance, pause when you see that sunset and pay attention to this bright spot in your day. Or take time for a period of reflection at the end of the day and think about all the moments that day that made you feel good. This reinforces what's meaningful and valuable in your life, she says, motivating you and building self confidence. In short, paying attention to positive emotions helps breed more positive emotion.

Religion and Spirituality

Whenever Alison Boden feels stressed, she heads to Chicago's lakefront to walk and pray. "It helps me become less anxious," says Boden, dean of the University of Chicago's Rockefeller Chapel.

Her spiritual practice and faith may also provide her with protection from depression and heart disease, boost her immune system, keep her marriage strong, and lengthen her life. According to researchers, religious beliefs can reduce feelings of stress, lower risks of stress-related diseases, and improve health and happiness.

That's because religious faith helps us cope with life's major and minor stresses in a myriad of physical and emotional ways.

For instance, prayer, like meditation, can lower your blood pressure. Religious rituals offer you continuity and comfort when life's road becomes rocky. Worship services provide chances for social interaction. And faith-based teachings show you more constructive problem-solving methods and provide you with a sense of divine support.

"This isn't a cheap way of 'making nice' with the things that stress us out," Boden says. "This is about gathering the strength to go back out there and meet life's challenges."

Experts agree. "Religious resources provide a way of making sense of the trauma and tribulations that goes beyond the secular interpretation," says Kenneth Pargament, Ph.D., professor of psychology at Bowling Green State University in Ohio. "We see an opportunity for growth or to become closer to God. It provides meaning to the worst of life's situations."

Religious faith boosts our spirits on ordinary days, too, by encouraging us to see life more optimistically. "If we could do this naturally, that would be great. But most of us can't," says Harold G. Koenig, M.D., author of *The Healing Power of Faith* and director of Duke University's Center for the Study of Religion/Spirituality and Health.

"We look at the things in life that are missing and complain about our unfilled expectations," he says. "Religion forces us to take a more positive view, to be grateful, to forgive others. All good things that lead to optimism and better health."

SPIRITUALITY FOR THE NONRELIGIOUS

Interested in spirituality but uncomfortable with traditional religion? Simply look within.

"We're already connected with our souls and the divine," says Barbara Ardinger, Ph.D., author of *Practicing the Presence of the Goddess: Everyday Rituals to Transform Your World.* "We're connected all the time. We just think we're disconnected."

While spirituality itself hasn't been studied as much as religious faith for its long-term health effects, it's still just as likely to help you relax and feel less stressed.

Here's what Dr. Ardinger suggests.

Create rituals. Keep flowers on your desk. Drink your morning coffee from a certain cup. "The repeatability and predictability of our little, unencumbered rituals add a bit of security in our age of chaos," she says.

Seek like-minded women. Women's groups that organize at bookstores, women's centers, or places of worship can provide emotional and spiritual support. "We need community to help us through the ragged times," says Dr. Ardinger.

Make an altar. Fill a shelf with meaningful objects: a photograph of your grandmother, a shell from the beach, a cherished dish. "It's just a small collection, per se," Dr. Ardinger says, "but symbolically, it's a hook to bring us back to our inner selves, an anchor to hold us for a few minutes, at least, to our spiritual reality."

firm. "People feel more connected to each other. They feel closer to their faith, God, and themselves."

Not to mention less stressed.

Of course, cultivating such spirituality requires time and attention. "We want fast, immediate, sweatless relief," says Rabbi Nancy Flam of Northampton, Massachusetts, director of the Spirituality Institute at Metivta, a retreat-based learning program for rabbis and Jewish lay leaders. "Developing a spiritual life takes discipline. That doesn't mean the activities need to be onerous—just regular."

The hardest thing about a spiritual practice?

"Carving out the time," says Boden.

A flexible attitude helps. "A spiritual practice can be anything at any time," Flam says. "It depends on our intentions—that we want to stand in the presence of the divine and cultivate awareness, which we can do just by taking our dog for a walk."

Here are some ways to begin integrating spirituality into your daily life.

Take inventory. List everything for which you're grateful, from your husband to your office window, and post it on your computer or somewhere else where you'll see it every day. It will remind you, even on tense days, of your blessings.

Give thanks. In the Jewish tradition, just awakening each morning warrants a blessing, says Flam, who says that such acts have a practical benefit: "You don't begin your day with an

Beyond Sunday Morning

Yet spirituality's power to soothe often goes untapped as we limit faith to Sunday mornings or family crises, denying ourselves its daily emotional and physical effects.

"Bringing a conscious awareness into everyday life has multiple benefits," says Krista Kurth, Ph.D., cofounder of Renewal Resources in Potomac, Maryland, a management consulting immediate flood of anxiety, wondering how you are ever going to get everything done in time."

Pray actively. Whenever Boden sits down to pray, her mind shifts into organizing overdrive. "I start making my to-do list. I think about the laundry and the people I need to call," she admits. So instead of sitting and praying, she walks and prays, giving herself a physical distraction that helps her spiritual concentration.

Recite a personal mantra. "We're so used to putting ourselves down: 'I'm so tired. I'm so stressed,'" says Dr. Kurth. Instead, she suggests, silently repeat "I'm full of peace" or "I honor God within me" when we're on hold, in traffic, or waiting in line. "Saying a spiritual phrase replaces those negative thoughts and breaks the cycle of negativity."

Read reflectively. Instead of scanning headlines, pick a Psalm, prayer service, or poem, and read for insight, a practice known as *lectio divina.* "Give yourself 15 minutes to let the text speak to you," advises Boden.

Find a spiritual home. Solitary spirituality "is a pretty lonely venture," says Boden, who suggests calling your faith's local district offices. "Tell them you're looking for a modern liturgy in a place that welcomes women's leadership. They'll understand what you're saying."

See the divine in ordinary things. "Looking for the spiritual

ON THE FRONT LINES
A Priest

As an Episcopal priest in New Haven, Connecticut, Barbara Cheney, 58, spends her days—and often her evenings—caring for her 200-person congregation. It's a small yet challenging church, given its economic, racial, and demographic diversity. But Cheney, who was among the first wave of women to be ordained as Episcopal priests, sees her job not as a source of stress but as a chance to view God at work.

Cheney began considering the ministry in her thirties, after she became very involved in her church. By the time she decided to go to the seminary, the Church had decided to ordain women as priests. She says, "It was so wonderful to find the doors open to me."

There are still people within the Church who struggle with women's ordination, says Cheney. "That's a challenge men don't face—where the question isn't whether you're the right person for the job but whether you come embodied in the right flesh and blood. I'm very fortunate in my ministry that people have worked that out before inviting me to be their pastor."

Instead, for her the most stressful thing is continually marshaling her church's resources: its aging building, its finances, and its congregation's gifts and talents. With members' high commitment to community outreach, she says, much of their inner nurturing falls to her. "It makes for some long weeks, but it's wonderfully exciting to see people come alive in their faith or have a transforming experience."

To care for herself, Cheney seeks spiritual support from others. She meets weekly with a handful of local clergy, and they share their concerns and pray together. Each month, she also meets with her spiritual director, whose role is to help her know God's presence in her life. She says, "These relationships have been wonderful for me; as a priest, I can get so caught up in preparing a sermon or caring for someone else that my own spiritual life gets put on the back shelf if I'm not careful."

SPIRITUALITY IN THE WORKPLACE

The fresh-baked cookies alone are probably enough to draw a crowd.

But the nurses, doctors, and other workers at the University of California, Los Angeles, UCLA Medical Center don't follow the chaplain and her pushcart of tea and cookies simply to take advantage of some free food; they gather instead for a few special moments of spiritual rest.

Billed as a "tea for the soul," it's a precious chance for medical caregivers to restore their own spirits with conversation, prayer, or even tears. "Sometimes a neonatal nurse who's lost four babies that week just needs to cry—something she certainly can't do on the floor," says the Reverend Sandra Yarlott, director of clinical pastoral education and one of a dozen chaplains at the hospital. "Afterward, she's in a much more centered and giving place."

Such a gathering seems natural for a workplace like a medical center, where employees confront life and death daily. But hospitals aren't the only employers offering spiritual events these days. Whether you work in a real estate firm or a fast-food restaurant, your opportunities to do "soul work" at work are rapidly expanding, from prayer groups to meditation rooms.

Cynics might pin this trend on our increasingly long work hours, but Krista Kurth, Ph.D., co-founder of Renewal Resources in Potomac, Maryland, sees the growth of spirituality in the workplace differently. "The baby boomers are reaching midlife," she says, a point at which we begin evaluating our lives in a less material, more spiritual context.

For many of us, priorities begin to change, she says. "We're interested in living a more integrated life because it's difficult, painful, and deadening to do things that don't match with our values."

Adding an element of spirituality to our workday activities can also ease the pressures of even the most demanding jobs. "Health care is so stressful right now," says UCLA clinical specialist Malou Blanco Yarosh, R.N. "Nurses are working harder, patients are sicker, and hospital stays are getting shorter." Those are big issues, but somehow, she says, the teas for the soul help.

"There is this incredible sense of, as a professional caretaker, always giving out," says Katherine Brown-Saltzman, R.N., a clinical specialist at UCLA Medical Center and assistant clinical professor at UCLA School of Nursing. "To have this moment—even if you're only passing by the doorway—is a reminder that there's a place and need for us to stop and be cared for, too."

in the moment is really important for women," says Dr. Kurth, because we often don't have time for anything else. If we think of all that we do as an offering to the divine, we can see the spiritual in everyday acts: washing the dishes, playing with our kids, or talking to our husbands at dinner.

Spirituality at Work

From impossible deadlines to difficult colleagues, the workplace can be a never-ending source of tension. Yet it doesn't have to stress us out, thanks to the perspective that spirituality can offer. "In the face of frustration, we can pause and look at the bigger picture," Dr. Kurth says.

Honoring our spiritual selves on the job also helps us in other ways. "We get more out of work," she says. "It's more than just an attitude—it's an emotional and physical change. We're less hunched-over. We're more openhearted. We have more energy."

Here's how you can blend your spiritual and professional lives, even in today's diverse workplaces.

Take a spiritual break. Use your lunchtime for meditation, prayer, or spiritual reading—whatever soothes your soul during hectic times.

Remember the Golden Rule. We often reap what we sow, so always treat colleagues with that adage in mind.

Serve your staff. Being the boss shouldn't be about ordering employees around; it should be about providing your staffers with all of the tools and support that they need to do their jobs in meaningful ways.

Be charitable. Practice your spirituality in a practical way by organizing an event that benefits others, such as a food drive or a fund-raising event such as a 5-K run. You'll help your community and build deeper relationships among your coworkers.

Remember: God's the ultimate boss. "We can get caught up in thinking we're responsible for outcomes," Dr. Kurth says. "Offering our work to God reminds us that we're just stewards, that we don't have control."

DE-STRESSING PLACES
A Labyrinth

To the uninitiated, a labyrinth looks like a life-size maze, full of twisting turns, false leads, and dead ends.

But labyrinths, developed in medieval times as a safe substitute for religious pilgrimages to Jerusalem, seek not to confuse and frustrate but to clarify and illuminate. With only one path in and out of the circular pattern, you'll never get lost in a labyrinth—just in your own thoughts.

That type of quiet mindfulness—essential to keeping stress under control—is a rare experience for women today, says the Reverend Patricia Hunt. "The way we get good at being modern Americans is by multitasking," says Hunt, chaplain for Mary Baldwin College in Staunton, Virginia, which uses labyrinths. "But we're losing the ability to lose ourselves entirely in something we choose to do," she says.

Labyrinths can help—especially if you are too fidgety for meditation. "It's a tool that's particularly helpful to the Western mind," says Marney Gibbs, a labyrinth facilitator and retired psychotherapist in Staunton. "The Eastern mind is accustomed to sitting quietly, but the Western mind is so goal-oriented that it's very difficult for us to sit. Walking, we can do."

As a result, labyrinths, which range from an outdoor path marked by rocks to a printed canvas floor cloth, have become increasingly popular, particularly among women.

"Somehow that archetypal pattern has the effect of connecting us to our inner wisdom and giving us the strength to bolster ourselves," says Donna Stetser, R.N., Reiki Master–Usui Shiki Ryoho, who with her partner built a stone labyrinth 40 feet in diameter on their Fairview, North Carolina, property in 1995.

Perhaps that's because a labyrinth often mirrors how we approach life. "It's a journey, and there's no right or wrong way to do it," Gibbs says. "You can do it together or alone. Some hurry; others take their time. Some always give way to those they meet on the path. If you watch the process as you go through, you'll learn something about yourself."

Making New Connections

Stress can sneak up on us like a runaway shopping cart barreling toward our brand-new car in the grocery store parking lot. It gains momentum, the sharp metal edges charging at the gleaming paint . . . until some kind bystander dives between car and cart and absorbs the impact. Like that bystander, social support can step in and buffer us against the abrasive effects of stress.

And when it comes to making those stress-reducing connections, women have the edge. We give one another more frequent and effective social support, we're quicker to provide help when a friend is stressed, and we're more satisfied overall with our personal connections than men.

In fact, new studies suggest we have our own, unique way to deal with stress, called "tend and befriend," that's more effective than the fight-or-flight mechanism we've always been thought to use.

Reducing Stress with Friendship

"Social support is emotionally nurturing, and if it's emotionally nurturing, it's going to be physically nurturing—the classic mind-body connection," says Patricia McWhorter, Ph.D., a licensed psychologist in Palm Harbor, Florida, and author of *Cry Our Native Soul*.

More specifically, social support has many benefits.

It calms. Stress produces physiological responses, including increased heart rate, breathing, and blood pressure, that over time can harm mental and physical health. "And social support cuts off this dysfunctional cycle," says Judith C. Tingley, Ph.D., psychologist and public speaker in Phoenix.

A study reported in the *Journal of Behavioral Medicine* found that women experienced high blood pressure and heart rates only when they performed stressful tasks alone, compared with those who did them with a female friend or even a with a female stranger. In the latter case heart rate and blood pressure responses were minimal. Just having a woman in the room, whether she was a stranger or a friend, reduced stress.

This calming power appears to work over the long term, too. People who have social connections bounce back more quickly from surgeries and illnesses than those without support. For instance, breast cancer patients who are in support groups live longer than those who don't join such groups.

It takes a load off. When you have solid social connections, you have people who are prepared to help, whether it's a lift to work or someone to care for your children in an emergency. "There are people there to say, 'Don't worry, we've got this covered,' which reduces stress," says David Posen, M.D., a public speaker in Oakville, Ontario, and author of *Always Change a Losing Game.*

Social support may also help stop stress from starting in the first place. For example, if you face work conflict but have sufficient social support from your colleagues, you'll be less likely to view the problem as stressful.

It dissolves upset. We feel much better when we talk things through. "And when we hear ourselves talk, we can often get to the root of what's bothering us without the listener saying a word," says Dr. Posen.

It validates. If someone listens empathetically and says things like "Gee, that must be hard" or "I agree," or "That happened to me, too," it makes us feel better, says Mark Gorkin, licensed clinical social worker, president of StressDoc Enterprises, and author of *Practice Safe Stress*. "You begin to feel like you're not alone or a freak of nature after all," he says.

It boosts self-esteem. "Anything that

FIGHT OR FLIGHT: MADE FOR A MAN

It seems that, unlike certain deodorants, the classic fight-or-flight stress response isn't *really* made for a woman. Even though women initially show signs of the fight-or-flight reaction, we also have our own unique response, called "tend and befriend."

First coined in 1932 by Walter Cannon, the term *fight or flight* refers to our instinct to either put up our dukes or run like hell when faced with a stressor. But like most scientific studies, until recently most fight-or-flight experiments were performed with males (especially male rats) for fear that females' menstrual cycles would confound results. But by excluding females, scientists overlooked an entire instinctual stress response—the female one. The results of a landmark study conducted by Shelley Taylor, Ph.D., professor of psychology at UCLA, suggest that our stress response can be better defined as a turning to one another for nurturance and support.

For example, a series of studies revealed that when fathers had stressful workdays, they were likely to withdraw from their families (flight), but when mothers had stressful workdays, they showed additional affection to their children (tend and befriend).

Dr. Taylor's study also linked oxytocin, the hormone typically associated with labor and breastfeeding, to the female stress response. We release it when we're stressed, and it acts like a sedative, reducing fear and physiological stress responses such as fast heartbeats and breathing. It may also hormonally encourage us to nurture our children and befriend fellow women.

---

threatens our self-esteem (for instance, someone's threatening or criticizing us) produces a stress response," says Dr. Posen. Our social connections help us feel better about ourselves—good friends make us feel good, and we feel as if we're part of a larger whole. "And as self-esteem improves, stress diminishes," he says.

LET A PET SOOTHE YOUR STRESS

He's always there when you need him, and he looks at you with love no matter how grouchy you are. No, not your husband. Your dog (or cat, or gerbil, or ferret).

Studies show that just petting a dog or cat has such a calming effect, it actually lowers blood pressure. Also, cardiac patients do better when they have a pet during their recovery process. And a Croatian study found that children with pets coped better with war-related post-traumatic stress disorder than children without pets.

"I think animals are God's gift to us for sanity," says Patricia McWhorter, Ph.D., a licensed psychologist in Palm Harbor, Florida, and author of *Cry Our Native Soul*. Pets love us unconditionally. "They don't judge us, tell us our outfit looks horrible, or ask to borrow the car keys," she says.

"Pets also act as a distraction and a mood elevator," says Judith Siegel, Ph.D., professor of public health and associate dean at the UCLA School of Public Health. And they provide an opportunity to care for something, which makes us feel needed.

Any type of pet—bird, hamster, rabbit—provides a sense of companionship. "But I think people feel less lonely when they can really interact with a pet," says David Posen, M.D., public speaker in Oakville, Ontario, and author of *Always Change a Losing Game*. "If you sit and watch a fish, the very act of sitting and watching can be calming, but there's not much interaction," he says. So while any pet with a heartbeat will reduce stress, the maximum benefit may come from a dog or cat.

It lingers. "Social support instills a kind of inner foundation—you carry around the beliefs and sharing that you receive from your social connections even when they're not there, like that great teacher you had in high school who remains a role model throughout your life," says Gorkin.

Female Friends: The Ultimate Connection

When they're stressed, female prairie voles prefer to be around other female prairie voles. The same goes for humans. It seems that social support from women is more stress relieving to both women and men than social support from men.

A study at the University of California, San Diego, recorded the blood pressure responses of men and women who gave a 5-minute impromptu speech to either a male or a female audience. Even though the audiences behaved identically, the speakers had lower blood pressure when they talked before a female audience. "We're not sure why this is," says study researcher Nicholas Christenfeld, Ph.D., associate professor of psychology. "But we suspect it may be because the speakers interpreted the support differently when it came from women. When it came from men, the support was interpreted as 'I understand what you're saying, and you're making good points,' but when it came from a woman, it was interpreted as 'I like you as a person.'"

It seems that females are just more socially wired than males are. "Our connections are more naturally feelings-based," says Dr. McWhorter. A landmark anthropology study illustrated this difference, she says. Researchers watched two opposing tribes of chimpanzees. The males from each tribe waited at the imaginary line of territory, throwing rocks and chasing one another away. Meanwhile, the females sneaked into one another's trees, where they secretly bonded, groomed one another, and played with one another's infants.

Finding Your Own Connections

Although simply being a woman provides an advantage when it comes to making connections, there's more you can do. Here are some ways to build social networks (or strengthen the ones you already have).

Be supportive yourself. "Our mothers told us when we were little: 'To have a friend, you have to be a friend,' " says Karyn Buxman, R.N., president of HUMORx, a company that helps people feel better about themselves and their work through humor and laughter, and author of *This Won't Hurt a Bit!* The amount of social support we give is as important as how much we get. Follow these guidelines to be a good supporter.

- ❥ Ask questions, and show interest in what the other person has to say.
- ❥ Just listen. "Don't judge or tell the person what she should do—that's the last thing we need when we need social support," says Dr. McWhorter.
- ❥ Nurture your friendships with regular phone calls, invitations, and support.
- ❥ When something is shared with you in confidence, don't tell your five best friends.

Focus on quality, not quantity. A study at Yale University found that people with just a few friends who felt loved and supported had fewer coronary blockages than those with many friends who felt less loved and supported. These are some characteristics necessary for quality social connections.

Compassion. "To feel supported, you have to feel cared for and understood," says Dr. Tingley.

Unconditional love. "You need to feel safe to be vulnerable, goofy, and free to let it all hang out," says Dr. McWhorter.

Accessibility. Quality social support is there for you whenever you need it, even at 4 o'clock Monday morning.

Trustworthiness. "You want someone who won't ridicule you or let the whole world know about your problem," says Linda Sapadin, Ph.D., a psychologist practicing in Valley Stream, New York, and author of *It's About Time: The Six Styles of Procrastination and How to Overcome Them.*

Honesty. Someone who constantly tells you you're wonderful isn't going to be much help. "Find someone who can listen but also be objective," says Gorkin.

Know what to avoid. When it comes to spilling your guts, it's smart to look out for the red flags. Dr. Posen recommends you zip it up when you notice the following traits.

Cattiness. Someone who reveals others' confidences to you is also likely to reveal yours to them.

Otherworldliness. If you're having relationship problems because of your infertility, a happily married woman with three children may not be able to empathize. Choose someone you can relate to on this particular issue.

Self-centeredness. The woman who immediately switches the focus of the conversation from your problem to herself probably won't be much help.

Disinterest. If she seems impatient when you're talking, she probably isn't interested, so you should talk to someone else.

Insensitivity. If she's uncaring when she talks about others, she's probably not going to be too caring with you either.

Start with what you have. "You may not have to build a support system—you may just have to start being more open with the people you already know," says Dr. Posen. Your "fun friend" (with whom you've never pondered anything deeper than what kind of martini to order) may turn out to be a great listener.

BLAME IT ON STRESS

Depression

Like water against a dam, stress can build and finally push us to collapse into depression. "When a woman's own coping mechanisms fail or there is a lack of social support to help cope, the stress can become overwhelming and debilitating and lead to feelings of depression," says Liane Colsky, M.D., a physician practicing in Los Angeles.

Depression comes in many shapes and sizes. The most severe cases appear to be genetically or chemically determined. "Most of the other forms of depression, commonly referred to as 'the blues' or 'feeling down in the dumps,' appear to be stress-related—they result when the pressures of daily living overwhelm a woman's ability to cope,'" says Dr. Colsky.

And stress-related depression can spin into a vicious cycle. A woman who's depressed will have low energy levels and difficulty motivating herself to get things done, which leads to more stress and hence more depression. "And problems will appear to be totally unsolvable," says Dr. Colsky.

To break the cycle and avoid stress-related depression, try to stay active, through exercise, running errands, or even volunteering. "Work to focus your thoughts away from yourself and the fact that you're feeling down in the dumps," she says. You must force yourself to come up above the depressive state." To do this, she recommends setting goals, no matter how small. "Set up a routine to take a step toward the goal each day, even if it's a small baby step," she says. "Then, when you have reached your goal, immediately set another goal—having a continuum of goals to attain will lift you out of depression."

Talk to strangers. "It's often easier to confide in strangers than friends because you don't have to worry about them telling others you know, and you don't have to worry about damaging their opinion of you," says Dr. Sapadin. Support groups and group therapy provide excellent opportunities for stranger interaction

Join a group. If you run for exercise, join a running group. If you read, join a book club. If you want to do something for the community, volunteer. "You'll meet people with common interests, and they'll also be doing some things you're not doing, which can challenge you to stretch and grow," says Gorkin.

Go online. The Internet helps build social bridges among diverse groups of people. "In some chat groups, people come together and are honest with one another," says Gorkin. "They gradually open up and meet people with whom they can create a one-on-one relationship."

The proof: A study reported in the *American Journal of Community Psychology* gave 42 single women computer-mediated social support (CMSS) concerning parenting issues. The online discussions revealed close personal relationships among the women, and the mothers who regularly participated in CMSS experienced less parenting stress.

Online groups are also great if you want to remain anonymous. But as with all Web information, consider the source and be cautious. Visit the site a few times before you decide to join. Good starting points for online support groups include www.liszt.com, www.drkoop.com, and www.psychcentral.com.

In Your Spare Time

Ever notice how the busiest woman you know also seems to have the time to sew her own curtains, bake her own bread, or grow a summer's worth of salads every season? And yet she never appears half as frazzled as you do just trying to get through 8 hours of work and the dinner hour. What's her secret?

It could be her hobbies.

"My experience has shown that those who handle stress best are those who have found a pastime that lifts their spirit," says Washington, D.C., psychotherapist Mark Gorkin, a licensed clinical social worker and author of *Practice Safe Stress with the Stress Doc*. Whether you collect stamps or keep a scrapbook, whittle or paint, make jewelry or sing in a barbershop quartet, you'll find yourself renewed and refreshed in a way that just plopping yourself in front of the television set could never do.

A hobby is your "happy time," says Gorkin, that slice of the day that helps you recharge from the flurry of family/work/community obligations. It enables you to disconnect from your concerns for a while and shift your brain into a creative, constructive mode. This shift in focus,

in turn, alleviates the most serious side effects of stress—high blood pressure, high cholesterol, and heart disease. "I believe that spending more than 1 hour a week on a hobby you love will cut your risk of a heart attack," he says.

Call it a hobby, a pastime, or play, but any activity that produces emotions of joy or the experience we call fun is essential for health, says O. Carl Simonton, M.D., director of the Simonton Cancer Counseling Center in Pacific Palisades, California. That's because emotions significantly influence health, and positive emotions affect our health in a positive manner.

Play and hobbies force us to change our perspective, to suspend our limits, to make up our own rules and change them, he says. They improve our quality of life by knocking us out of despair.

Culturally, however, the pursuit of a hobby is not recognized as a relaxation technique the way meditation or deep breathing is, says Douglas Chay, a licensed clinical social worker and a stress therapist at Mercy Medical Center in Baltimore. Yet just like these more high-profile practices, he says, "a hobby gives your conscious

FIND PURPOSE WITH "SERIOUS LEISURE"

The seemingly contradictory term *serious leisure* describes the pastimes of passionate hobbyists and amateurs, says Robert Stebbins, Ph.D., faculty professor of sociology at the University of Calgary in Alberta and author of *After Work: The Search for an Optimal Leisure Lifestyle*, who coined the expression in 1982.

These people are not "hamming-around dabblers," says Dr. Stebbins, but rather trained practitioners of an activity with rules. They're the amateur fine artists whose work challenges that of professionals, or the community group actors who could tread the boards of Broadway.

Immersion into a serious leisure activity produces a feeling of well-being on several fronts, says Dr. Stebbins. First, it provides the hobbyist with an identity often totally separate from her normal life. She becomes defined by achievements, irrespective of her job or family, and as her prowess grows, she earns the respect of other practitioners, bolstering her self-esteem. Serious leisure activities normally offer a sense of community, he says, along with a configuration of social events. If you're involved in astronomy, there's undoubtedly a local club to join, but also a national and international group. Magazines and conferences link you to like-minded others. "Now that you're socially located, you're no longer a grain of sand adrift in the universe," he says.

While the performance requirements of these pastimes may bring some stress to your life, it's usually positive stress because you entered into the activity freely, says Dr. Stebbins, and you can always back out if it gets to be too much. Sometimes the stress comes from facing a fear, like performing. Yet once these demons are tackled, serious hobbyists feel good about themselves because they've triumphed over adversity.

Perhaps the best way to understand serious leisure is to contrast it with casual leisure, says Dr. Stebbins. Casual leisure, like watching television, doesn't bolster self-esteem, doesn't require a lot of skill, rarely offers a special community, and doesn't foster well-being. "Many people watch TV during their leisure hours," he says, "but I don't know anyone who proudly defines herself as a TV viewer."

mind a break from the stress tapes playing in your mind" by diverting your attention away from the cares of the day. By the time a person seeks help from a therapist like him, Chay says, stress has become a real problem in their lives. His clients tend to put their own needs last on the list, but a hobby forces them, in a pleasurable way, to do something strictly for themselves. When they take up a hobby, he says, they're amazed at how much it helps: "The difference in how someone feels can truly be like night and day."

For instance, Web site developer Joyce Cutler of San Francisco found soap making helped her "turn off" work. Mixing emollients and fragrances "takes me far away from my everyday pressures," she says. Within a month of starting this hobby, Joyce found that the chronic tightness in her chest disappeared and the whirl of her life slowed. Her job is just as demanding, "but it doesn't get to me in the same way," she says, "because I have this one bright spot in the week that's just for me."

It's a Control Thing

Most stress springs from a feeling that you're not in control, but a hobby puts you in control, says Chay. For instance, if you want to paint blue roses on a tin bread box, who's going to stop you? You may think little junk toys look great glued onto picture frames, or you might decide to build a footstool out of broken tree limbs. Nobody can say what's "right" or "wrong" for you and your hobby, says Chay, and this freedom is empowering. Thus you stop feeling like a victim. When that happens, physiological stress reactions ease up, a sense of well-being sets in, and you gain a proper perspective on life, one that better enables you to cope with stress in the future.

And, for perhaps the only time in your life, the end result doesn't matter. So what if the birdhouse leans to the left or the paint on the model airplane is smudged? What's important is that you built the birdhouse or painted the plane. It's the process that counts, not the product.

"There are precious few arenas in our culture where the final result isn't important," says Chay. "The need to do well is a major source of stress for most of us, but with hobbies, that really doesn't matter."

It's a Relaxation Thing

Another reason to pull out the cross-stitch or fire up the kiln is that focusing on a pleasurable hobby triggers your relaxation response, not unlike visualization or meditation. Throwing pottery, for example, demands your full concentration if you don't want lopsided pots, Chay says, and that focus on an immediate activity blots out all the demands and annoyances that are stressing you out. "With a hobby, you must be 'in the moment,'" he

THE SECRET ART OF DOING NOTHING

Doing nothing is the most complex "simple activity" there is, admits Mark Gorkin, a Washington, D.C., licensed clinical social worker and psychotherapist who bills himself as the "Stress Doc."

Initially, the challenge is withdrawing from the "always on" state of mind, says Gorkin, the internal push that directs us to constantly do something, anything. Even if you have the time and freedom to just plop yourself into an easy chair and stare at the wall, if you're like most people, you'll find it difficult to stop thoughts from racing through your mind.

To calm this internal tide of thoughts, channel a state of "relaxed attention." Open up to a slower, gentler pace through a quietly observant mode of "being." Sit quietly and practice being a silent observer, he says, even if thoughts continue banging in your head. Disconnecting from the hurly-burly takes effort at first, says Gorkin, but remind yourself that restorative relaxation demands nonconstructive time, that it's good for you, and that eventually those stress messages ping-ponging through your mind will fade.

Modern life has conditioned us to think that we have to relentlessly strive, push, and achieve. In truth, says Gorkin, a successful life has balance—periods of full-tilt activity, periods of park bench contemplation. Most of us have learned too well how to push ourselves, he says, and, although it runs counter to the cultural mantra of "more, more, more," we can learn to pull back, to mentally unplug. Lolling in a bubble bath listening to Mozart may not push you up the corporate ladder, but it will give your inner resources a chance to recharge. In fact, it is exactly this recharge that allows you to achieve your goals, he says.

In a world where we constantly feel we must "do," give yourself permission to just "be," says Gorkin.

The ability to fully relax involves adjustments in the physical and psychological realms, says Gorkin, and it doesn't happen overnight. It requires patience, but the struggle is worth it when you realize how critical relaxation is for optimal mind-body health.

says, so all those fretful thoughts about your crabby boss or noisy neighbors can't be center stage. For the span of time you're focused on that particular activity, everything else essentially ceases to exist in your conscious mind, giving you a chance to recuperate from stress.

You're tapping into the second side of your mind, says Chay, entering an alpha state. When your mind enters this different "space," you shift your focus away from everyday stressors and concentrate your attention on something entirely disconnected. After all, how can you continue to mentally stew over that snide crack from your boss when it takes every bit of concentration to get the mast placed just right on that ship in a bottle?

It's a Self-Esteem Thing

Apart from calming your mind, hobbies enable you to feel better about yourself, Chay says. If you've cooked a fabulous meal, fostered a cutting garden, or won a blue ribbon in the horse jumping trials, you've also short-circuited those stress-producing feelings of "I can't do it well enough" or "I can't get everything done." "Hobbies boost your self-esteem by showing you you're competent," he says. In the process, your hobby reminds you that you are a multifaceted, whole person, he says, not just your job title or family role.

For instance, career counselor and mother of three Ricki Wagner, of Cincinnati, began making paper as a way "to do something that was just about me." Starting with an interest in the process and an inexpensive kit intended for children, Wagner taught herself "all about pulp" and has become so skilled she now sells her handmade paper at craft fairs. This creativity inhabits a realm independent from the rest of her life, she says, and "makes the rest of my life richer because I feel so good about myself."

Finding a Hobby

While creative activity stimulates many positive mental and physical reactions, getting stressed-out people to try it is often a struggle, says Karyn Buxman, R.N., a stress reduction specialist in Hannibal, Missouri.

In our society, which stresses the Puritan work ethic, it's difficult for people to learn how to lose themselves in play, says Dr. Simonton, and many of us are taught early on not to play. By the time we're adults, he says, we've internalized those voices.

That's particularly true when we're stressed, says Buxman. Just when we need the relaxation of play and hobbies, we're typically so fried we can't think of one fun thing to do.

The antidote: Develop a play list of 10 to 20 things you consider fun and relaxing.

Everyone thinks *something* is fun, says Buxman, even though we tend to push these thoughts to the back of our serious, adult minds. It may take some poking around your cerebral junkyard, she says, but you can find some hobby interest if you try. Think about something that's intrigued you, something you always wanted to know more about, she suggests. Or flash back to your childhood—was there some craft activity you really enjoyed? If you're still stumped, mull over your priorities. If you love taking pictures of your family but hate the fact that the photos end up in shoeboxes, scrapbooking may be a natural choice.

Ideally, says Buxman, half of these activities should cost $5 or less. When people are stressed out, a lack of money often figures in to the equation, she says. It costs nothing to go on a leaf-gathering safari. Inexpensive markers and a coloring book will set you back only a few bucks. Or sing in a local choir.

The type of hobby doesn't matter, says Buxman. What's important is your perception of it. You might consider the nuances of Civil War coin collecting mind-boggling and highly stressful, but someone else may find it the height of relaxation.

Buxman recommends at least 30 minutes of "fun time" each day. For most overstressed people, that seems like a daunting assignment, she admits, so start out small with 5 or 10 minutes each day, then build up. The goal, says Buxman, is to make your hobby a habit.

"You need to adjust your attitude, realize you need to bring fun into your life," she says. "It's not just a good idea—it's healthy. When people strike a balance between work and play, they find they feel better."

When Chay encounters clients who dismiss the idea of "hobby therapy," he frames it as a low-key challenge: "I tell them this will help you meet your goal of stress reduction—it can't hurt you—so why not give it a try?"

Although each person must define "play" for herself, some people adamantly insist that they can't find a hobby that interests them, says Gorkin, who calls himself the "Stress Doc."

If you feel like this, realize that may be a warning sign of depression, he says. Loss of interest in things you once enjoyed, or loss of vitality in general, is a common symptom of depression and should be discussed with a physician or therapist.

Once you take up a hobby, you have to educate people around you, says Chay. Your family may understand exercise or meditation as a stress-reduction tool but think needlepoint is frivolous. "You need to say, 'This is my time for myself,' and insist that they honor your chosen form of relaxation," he says.

Don't Bring Type A into Play

Given the nature of many Americans, we frequently apply our work attitudes to play, trading one form of stress for another. Thus we can become our own biggest stumbling block when it comes to the positive benefits of play, says Buxman, allowing type A personality competitiveness to creep in.

If you feel performance pressure starting to keep you from enjoying your hobby, ask yourself, "Why am I doing this?" If you feel that sense of "I have to," in order to keep up or prove yourself, then this hobby is not serving your stress-reduction needs, says Buxman. But if you feel like "I love it," despite rigorous requirements or an abundance of effort, then the activity is moving you into a very positive mindset.

The "hobby mind" should represent a paradigm shift away from the demands of our fast-paced, need-it-yesterday culture, says Buxman. This activity is a focused place to put your energies and, in doing so, de-stress and calm your mind. If it becomes just another way to compete or another source of anxiety, you've lost all the health-enhancing benefit, she says.

The Quiet: Meditation

Just 5 minutes every morning and 5 minutes every evening, and you can change your life. You don't need to quit your job, divorce your husband, or send your kids off to boarding school (not that those options may not sound appealing at times!).

Instead . . . just meditate. Only a few minutes twice a day, *every* day, can lead you away from your cares and concerns better than a bath full of bubbles, and transport you to a place where "being" is more important than "doing."

In her private practice in Washington, D.C., psychotherapist Annette Annechild, Ph.D., teaches virtually all her clients—men, women, and children—how to meditate. Having practiced meditation herself for the past 25 years, Dr. Annechild has seen firsthand what this "technique of stillness" can do. From helping her to lose weight, to "grounding" her, to guiding her from a career as a food and fitness writer to that of psychotherapist, nothing has been more powerful in her life than this one, simple act, she says. "It has altered me forever."

But just what *is* meditation?

Quite simply, it's listening to your inner voice, that gut feeling all of us have but too few of us listen to. We're so busy that we've lost touch with that voice, what Dr. Annechild calls our "authentic self."

Meditating—giving ourselves the opportunity to calm down and harness our energy—enables us to look inward, rather than outward. And there is nothing better, Dr. Annechild says, than the inner peace that can come from taking those few, precious moments for us.

It's more than inner peace, however, that meditation offers. It can actually help prevent—even cure—stress-related conditions, which some experts estimate account for up to 90 percent of doctors' visits. Headaches, insomnia, digestive problems, chronic pain, fatigue, skin conditions, and high blood pressure are just some of the medical problems linked to stress. Not to mention, of course, the emotional problems of depression: anger, cynicism, irritability, pessimism, and tension, all of which are problems that affect more and more women. Need proof? Women ages 40 and up are the fastest growing group claiming disability benefits for stress-related illness.

Meditation: 25 Years of Research

The benefits of meditation first began appearing in the medical literature more than 25 years ago and continue to do so today. It relaxes blood vessels, which lowers blood pressure. That in turn reduces your risk of heart disease.

A study from 2000 found that learning to relax and reduce stress through meditation may well reduce the risk of atherosclerosis and, with it, the risk of heart attack and stroke.

Identify the Cause

You would be hard-pressed to find anyone who'd argue that learning to relax is bad for you. But experts do suggest that before you start practicing any kind of meditation or relaxation technique, you identify just what it is that's causing your stress.

Women especially, says Lester Adler, M.D., medical director for the Sedona Center for Complementary Medicine in Arizona, frequently feel stressed not just because we're overscheduled and overworked but also because we've been encouraged from the time we were little girls to suppress—and repress—our anger. If that strikes a familiar chord, then just learning to relax may not be enough—at least not in the beginning.

"Learn to express yourself first," says Dr. Adler. "When you have become fully aware of that energy inside you, when you have learned to embrace it, express it, and then let it go, then you will be ready to sit quietly."

DE-STRESSING PLACES
A Color Spa

A day at a spa has always been a favorite way to relax. Just spending time being pampered can soothe even the most frazzled nerves. But many spa owners are realizing that relaxation is not just about looking good but also about feeling good. Many spas today are expanding their traditional spa services—such as massage therapy—to make room for more meditative or holistic treatments.

At the Away Spa in New York City's W Hotel, for example, color therapists believe that different colors spark different moods. In this popular spa treatment, which combines color therapy and hydrotherapy, you can have your aura "read" before being immersed in a soothing tub of colored, fragrant water.

First you have your photo taken with an "aura camera." The extremely light-sensitive film used in this specially designed camera is said to capture your personal energy field and translate it into colors. These colors coincide with the seven chakras (energy centers) of the body: violet, which represents the crown, or top of your head, and your spiritual self; indigo, for the brow, or your unconscious (or intuitive) self; blue, for the throat, or holistic thought; green, for the heart, or perfect love; yellow, for the solar plexus, or wisdom; orange, for the sacral, or belly button, area, or joy; and red, for the root (or pelvic area), or your physical self.

Based on the colors that appear in your photo, a color therapist prescribes a bath with the appropriate hues to augment your aura. If your aura reflects a lot of blues and greens, for example, you may find yourself in a bath filled with colored oils in reds and yellows for balance. To strengthen the effect, clients are given a pair of colored goggles to wear while relaxing in the tub.

GETTING WET: THE MAGIC OF HYDROTHERAPY

You know how relaxing a warm bath or soaking in a hot tub can feel. That's the essence of hydrotherapy, or the use of water, a practice that has been around for thousands of years. In fact, more than 5,000 years ago Hippocrates, the father of medicine, recommended bathing in natural hot springs as therapy for a host of medical conditions.

Hot—but not too hot (don't use water hotter than 102°F)—water not only can soothe your aching joints and muscles and improve your circulation but also can ease your tired mind. Don't use hydrotherapy if you have diabetes, high blood pressure, or heart disease or are pregnant or 65 or older, unless your doctor approves. Add a few drops of a pleasing essential oil—lavender is especially good for de-stressing and for promoting sleep—and your bath will be that much more relaxing.

The Right Meditation for You

Though there are a number of well-recognized forms of meditation and relaxation techniques, not every one may be right for you. Some may require more time than you're willing to give. Transcendental meditation (TM), for example, usually requires at least 20 minutes every morning and every evening. Others, such as biofeedback and hypnosis, generally require seeing (and paying for) a professional practitioner.

The important thing is to find the technique that works best for you so you'll continue to do it—preferably every day. Following are brief descriptions of some of the more common meditative and relaxation techniques.

Transcendental meditation (TM). TM was first brought to the United States by the Maharishi Mahesh Yogi in the 1960s and is probably the most popular form of meditation in the country today. Despite its Indian roots, TM doesn't conflict with any lifestyle or religion, says Robert Schneider, M.D., dean of the College of Maharishi Vedic Medicine at Marahrishi's University of Management in Fairfield, Iowa. And because it's so simple to do, you're more likely to actually do it every day. That's important because it's consistency that makes meditation particularly effective in reducing stress and providing long-term health benefits.

What distinguishes TM from other forms of meditation is that it _is_ so effortless, says Dr. Schneider. Other relaxation approaches involve doing _something_, even if that something is just concentrating on your breathing. TM, on the other hand, is a _lessening_ of activity both physiological and psychological, and that induces a deep state of rest, something many of us desperately need.

With TM, you typically concentrate on a sound or a word, known as a _mantra_ (from the Sanskrit words _man_, meaning "constant thinking," and _tra_, meaning "to be free"). While repeating your mantra to yourself, you are at the same time trying to reach a state of "detached observation." In other words, you are aware of your surroundings, but they do not distract you.

You may want to find a teacher or a guide to work with you in developing your meditation practice. But if you're anxious (no pun intended!) to get started now, you need a quiet, comfortable place and 15 to 20 minutes in which you can be alone and undisturbed. Sit in the same place for each meditation. Tie the practice in to a ritual: light a candle or burn incense. It doesn't matter what you choose; it just matters that you associate a certain place and a certain act with your meditation so you feel "in the mood."

Once you're comfortable, close your eyes and take a deep breath. Making your exhalations twice as long as your inhalations, simply focus on the action of your breath moving in and out. Then add your mantra, repeating the word or phrase you have chosen for yourself on both the inhaled breath and the exhaled breath.

It's not important what you use as your mantra, just that you use one. You may want to chant the commonly used *Om*, the mystical contemplation of ultimate reality. Or you may want to use a phrase that you find particularly meaningful, such as "peace," "shalom," or "let it be."

Don't worry if your mind starts to wander. In fact, accept the fact that when you're first beginning to meditate, it *will* wander. That doesn't mean you've "flunked" meditation. It simply means you're training your mind so that *you* are in control of *it*, not the other way around. Just be patient.

Progressive relaxation. When you practice progressive relaxation, you alternately contract and relax each of the major muscle groups in your body, trying to get your body to relax completely.

First, sit or lie down in a quiet, dark room. Begin by tensing a group of muscles, such as those in your right arm. Hold the contraction for 15 seconds, then release it while breathing out. After a brief rest, move on to another muscle group until you've gone through your entire

---

MUSIC HATH CHARMS

It probably comes as no surprise to you that different pieces of music can affect your mood. But it may come as a surprise to learn that clinical studies have actually confirmed this. Research shows that music can not only improve mood but also manage pain, reduce the need for sedatives and pain relievers during and after surgery, lessen nausea during chemotherapy, shorten hospital stays, relieve anxiety, lower blood pressure, ease depression, and enhance concentration and creativity. No one's exactly sure just how music heals, but it seems that the human brain is constructed in such a way as to respond to musical cues.

Recognizing the magic of music, hospitals across the country are calling on music therapists to work with patients including expectant mothers during labor and delivery and terminal cancer patients. In Boston, for example, music therapist Suzanne Hanser, Ed.D., sees oncology patients at the Zakim Center for Integrated Therapies at the Dana-Farber Cancer Institute. Dr. Hanser takes her 12-string lyre, alto recorder, and keyboard to patients' bedsides and plays, taking note of which melodies and instruments have the greatest effect on patients.

The best feedback she can get? "To see the patient simply fall asleep," she says.

---

body. You may find this especially helpful if you're having trouble sleeping at night.

Hypnosis. Hypnosis, which should be performed by a certified hypnotherapist (who can then teach you self-hypnosis techniques), induces a deeply relaxed state. While you are in this hypnotic state (sometimes known as a trance), the therapist can make suggestions that may encourage you to change your behavior or that offer relief of various symptoms. Most hypnosis practitioners are licensed in another health care profession, such as counseling, psychotherapy, or medicine, and use a clinical hypnosis certification as a complement to the

KEEPING IT SIMPLE

Browse your favorite newsstand or bookstore, and you'll see evidence of an antistress movement taking hold in this country. Generally known as "voluntary simplicity," the so-called simplicity movement represents the need many of us see for a less stressful, more meaningful life. Many magazines and books devoted to simplifying your life—whether that means "de-cluttering" your home, "downsizing" your career ambitions, or living off the land—have been published.

The contemporary voluntary simplicity movement began in 1981 with the publication of Duane Elgin's book *Voluntary Simplicity: Toward a Way of Life That Is Outwardly Simple, Inwardly Rich.* Today, Gerald Celente, founder and director of the Trends Research Institute in Rhinebeck, New York, estimates that about 5 to 7 percent of us are pursuing some form of voluntary simplicity.

Don't think that simplifying your life means doing without. It might—but it doesn't have to. Rather, the prevailing philosophy of today's voluntary simplicity movement is not necessarily to live without possessions or to live in frugality but to slow down and live a more balanced, deliberate, and thoughtful life. As our lives get more and more hectic, many of us are looking to the philosophy of Henry David Thoreau, who wrote in *Walden:*

> I went to the woods because I wished to live deliberately, to front only the essential facts of life, and see if I could not learn what it had to teach, and not, when I came to die, discover that I had not lived.

treatment they already provide. To find a trained hypnotherapist near you, send a self-addressed, stamped envelope to the American Society of Clinical Hypnosis, 130 East Elm Court, Suite 201, Roselle, Illinois 60172, or visit its Web site at www.asch.net.

Autogenic training (AT). AT, which is best learned through a practitioner trained in the technique, is a form of psychophysiologic therapy that teaches you to put yourself into a state of physical and mental relaxation similar to hypnosis. The exercises are designed to bring forth feelings of heaviness, warmth, a regular heartbeat, easy breathing, abdominal warmth, and a cool forehead. The idea behind AT is not to force your body into these states but to pretend you're already feeling these sensations; in time, your thoughts become self-fulfilling. Many hypnotherapists are trained in AT; you can check with the organization listed above.

Biofeedback. There are several types of biofeedback, most of which involve placing electronic sensors on various parts of your body. Brain wave biofeedback, for example, uses sensors placed on the scalp to measure electrical activity in the brain. Breathing biofeedback uses sensors placed around the chest and abdomen or around the mouth and nose to measure the rate, rhythm, and volume of your breathing. Electromyography measures muscle spasms and tension, finger pulse biofeedback measures pulse rate. Thermal biofeedback, via a temperature sensor taped to your finger, measures changes in bloodflow.

While you're hooked up to the sensors, a biofeedback therapist measures your body's reactions as your mind responds to various verbal prompts. Once you become aware of how certain thoughts stimulate certain responses, you may be able to learn how to control such nervous system functions as blood pressure, body temperature, and heart rate.

Mindfulness. Also known as nonconcentrative meditation, mindfulness meditation has its roots in Buddhist traditions. Unlike TM, mindfulness does not necessarily lead you to a deeply relaxed state but is designed more to help you become aware of yourself by observing your body's moment-to-moment changes. You first focus on your breathing and then on any other thoughts, feelings, or physical sensations you may be having, also known as your in-the-moment experiences.

In mindfulness meditation, as opposed to TM, these thoughts and feelings are not considered distractions that should be ignored. Instead, you should be aware of them as they unfold. Eventually, you should be able to experience events without being disturbed or stressed out about them.

To begin, find a sitting position that will be comfortable for 10 to 15 minutes. Take several deep breaths, inhaling and exhaling slowly, always breathing through your nose. Don't try to control your breathing in any other way; just breathe naturally. As you're breathing, begin to count—1 when you inhale, 2 when you exhale, 3 when you inhale, and so on until you reach 10. Don't get impatient if you lose count. Just re-

turn to 1 and start again. After you've practiced to the point where you no longer lose count (and that may take a month or two), you may want to simplify your meditation by simply saying "in" when you inhale and "out" when you exhale.

Once you become fully aware of your breathing, expand your focus to include the sensations of both your body and your surroundings—sights, smells, temperature, etc.

Guided imagery. Guided imagery encourages you to imagine certain scenes that help you relax. Need a vacation but can't get away? How about taking a mini-break? Just get comfortable and imagine that you're in your favorite setting. Perhaps that's the beach? "Feel" the soft sand between your toes, the warm sun on your face, the cool sea spray in your hair. The more detailed your images, the more convinced your body will be that you're actually there.

There's no set time for how long your mini-vacation should last. Thirty to 60 minutes is ideal, but if you can't manage that, even 5 to 10 minutes should do the trick if your images are detailed enough.

Take a Deep Breath

You're on in 3 minutes; the whole room is watching. Your heart's pounding, your face is flushed, your palms clammy. "Breathe," you tell yourself. You suck up a long, steady stream of air through your nose like a straw. But then your neck muscles tighten like a noose, the lump in your throat grows. You're lightheaded, dizzy; your concentration's shot. You fake a yawn for more air.

It's a scenario many of us are all too familiar with. A stressful event flips on the fight-or-flight switch and despite our best attempts to heed the quintessential anti-anxiety advice, focusing on our breathing only makes matters worse.

The problem is, what many of us think of as a deep breath is really a forceful *shallow* breath that only partially fills our lungs with air. As a result, we breathe more rapidly and experience an excessive loss of carbon dioxide. This, in the short term, affects our body's acid-base balance and prevents hemoglobin, the protein that carries oxygen in the blood, from releasing adequate oxygen to the brain and other organs.

Suddenly, you're hyperventilating. Your heart beats faster to pump more blood, your lungs and kidneys start working overtime, and your blood vessels constrict, turning our hands ice cold. Basically, your cells are close to suffocating.

Nature Unlearned

While the idea that we've actually forgotten how to breathe may sound ludicrous—after all, it is an involuntary function that we perform some 20,000 times a day—you need only compare the rise and fall of your own chest to that of a baby's to understand.

Infants breathe as nature intended. Their bellies stick out with each inhalation; their chests follow with a slight rise. Then everything sinks when they exhale.

But unlike infants, we live in a world of deadlines, PalmPilots, and cell phones. We run to work, to home, to the kids' soccer game, to the grocery store, or a cocktail party. Talking, eating, drinking, and exercising actually interfere with deep breathing, says Robert Fried, Ph.D., director of the Stress and Biofeedback Clinic at the Albert Ellis Institute in New York City and author of *Breathe Well, Be Well.*

But while it's necessary to stop breathing when we swallow, or to puff from the chest when we run, it's certainly not healthy to do so on a continual basis. And for most of us—especially in this culture of sucking in the gut for appearance's sake—catching a solid breath is as rare as a free trip to Paris.

Take Phyllis Ross, for example. This high school teacher from Camarillo, California, was over 50 before she mastered respiration. For much of her life, Phyllis felt tired and winded when stressed, and often woke at night gasping for air. After taking various antidepressants for 10 years to no avail, it finally hit her in October 1999: She didn't know how to breathe. A traumatic childhood had taught her early on to hold her breath when fearful. When she did exhale, it was shallow.

Today, after seeking private instruction from "breathing coach" Michael Grant White, following his Web site, www.breathing.com, and using his tapes, Phyllis no longer needs medication and hasn't woken up panic-stricken, gasping for air, in more than a year.

A Woman's Problem

Phyllis's story is far from unique. More and more people are turning to professionals for breathing lessons. Rich McCord, a certified yoga and meditation instructor at the Expanding Light Retreat in Nevada City, California, has seen his share of Silicon Valley refugees since 1983 and believes stress levels there have increased dramatically since the mid-1990s.

ARE YOU A CHEST BREATHER?

Do you lift your shoulders when you take a breath? Is your voice raspy, hoarse, or breathy? Do you sigh, gasp, or yawn frequently? If so, there's a good possibility that you're a shallow breather.

To find out for sure, place your hands on your torso, one over your chest and the other over your belly. Inhale. Notice which hand rises. If it's the top hand, you've now got confirmation for what you probably already suspected: you're a chest breather.

Even Dr. Fried marvels at the number of people, especially women, who pay $75 an hour to simply breathe with him in his office. "They live in penthouses, and yet they can't find a place to relax at home."

That could be a gender issue. When men have a stressful day at the office, for instance, they go home, vent, then relax, says Dr. Fried. Women, on the other hand, never get downtime. We come home to a second job: cleaning, cooking, taking care of the kids. In addition to our extra responsibilities, we're also less physically equipped than men to handle stress. The female hormone estrogen, at its peak, can *trigger* hyperventilation. To boot, our lungs are proportionally smaller than men's, so we naturally tend to breathe more quickly.

The Power of Breath

But deep breathing can do so much more than simply help us relax. It can make us *healthier.* "In case after case, patients have harnessed its power to lower blood pressure, prevent heart attacks, improve digestion, and ease migraines and asthma," says renowned alternative medicine expert Andrew Weil, M.D., director of

DE-STRESSING PLACES
A Silent Retreat

If you're like most women, there isn't a door in your house safe from the persistent rapping of knuckles, big or small. Blocking out quiet time and space to do breath work can be the biggest hurdle to learning the technique.

So, if you can, step outside of your life for a weekend—or longer. There are numerous centers that offer silent retreats or meditation training. If you can't get away, designate a corner of the house as "yours" for an hour and ask family members not to disturb you. Or find an empty conference room at work or a vacant corner at the library. When possible, practice in the same area. After time, you'll begin to associate a sense of relaxation simply upon entering that area, which will help your progress.

the program in integrative medicine and clinical professor of medicine at University of Arizona College of Medicine in Tucson. In fact, he says, "improper breathing is a common cause of ill health."

Breathing may well even help us live longer. The Framingham Study, which followed more than 3,000 men and women for a decade, found that people who breath well generally live longer. And a more recent study also turned up a significant relationship between healthy lung function and lifespan, after trailing nearly 1,200 people for 29 years.

But what's news to us Westerners has been a long-held truth in the East, where the old adage "Partial breathing is partial living" probably got its start. Yoga and meditation were integrated into Eastern culture centuries ago on the premise that deep, mindful breathing generates energy, or a spirit, within us called chi. The Chinese believe that chi can be considered a life force. Our bodies combine the life force from

the air we breathe with the life force from our food to provide us with our ability to live. Proper diet and breathing are necessary factors to healthy living.

Singer and voice teacher Nancy Zi, author of *The Art of Breathing*, agrees wholeheartedly. "*How* we breathe affects our every fiber," she says. "It is a way to acquire control over the mind and body. You can 'think' this inner energy to where needed."

When you breathe properly, says Zi, shyness fades, your voice becomes clearer, and your full personality emerges. The trick, she says, is to use nervous energy in your favor. "It's impossible to get rid of unwanted tension. We must *relocate* it."

And the place where we *send* our fear and anger, she says, is the "core," an intangible energy center located inches below the belly button. By directing your breath to the core, your tension will follow and melt, transforming into productive energy, she says.

Breathing 101

Of course, you don't have to believe in chi—or part with your nest egg for one-on-one lessons—to become a better breather. The same basic principles transcend East and West and can be done anywhere, anytime. When exhaling a deep breath, you can focus on melting the tension and negative energy you usually hold tightly in your chest. By melting this lump of tension and allowing it to drain as you exhale, you allow your tension to evaporate.

When you inhale properly, your diaphragm (the sheet of muscle that separates the lungs and the abdomen) relaxes downward, allowing your lungs to expand to bring in more air. Then when you exhale, the diaphragm contracts upward, toward the lungs, squeezing them like a vertically held accordion to push out all the air. This stimulates the vital organs within the abdomen, improving your overall health in many ways. Additionally, this abdominal deep breathing is calming and can reduce high blood pressure.

Unfortunately, many people aren't sure exactly where their diaphragm sits, which makes *using* it difficult. To get in touch with yours, McCord offers this simple exercise.

Lie on your back and place a small beanbag (about 2 pounds) on your belly, just below your rib cage and slightly above your navel. As you start inhaling, feel your lower abdomen begin to swell slightly upward with the breath. As the "wave" of swelling reaches the beanbag, smoothly push the bag upward with your abdomen. As you exhale, let the weight of the bag press into your belly and relax it. Do this twice a day for 10 minutes at a time.

To help you further grasp deep breathing, Zi offers this drill.

Stand erect but relaxed, imagining yourself as an upside-down eyedropper with the center of the bulb as your lower abdomen. Using your abdominal muscles, squeeze the air completely out of the eyedropper, then release. Let the bulb expand again and air will be drawn back into the body. Imagine that the opening of the glass tube ends where your throat and the back of your nose meet. Let the air flow in and out of this central opening.

FIND YOUR FUNNY BONE

What's invisible and can go up to 70 mph? Our breath as we *exhale* on the heels of a four-star joke.

Because laughing contracts the diaphragm and abdomen and forces out air at a much faster rate than normal, it also pulls *in* air much deeper. The result: automatic belly breathing.

Laughter is one of the best stress reducers we have, says Karyn Buxman, R.N., author of *This Won't Hurt a Bit!* and a registered nurse in Hannibal, Missouri, who offers clinics on therapeutic laughter across the country.

To boot, nearly every muscle in the body contracts, then releases, during laughter—including, to some degree, the heart—melting away physical tension to the point that we may wind up clinging to a counter to stand.

To fill your days with laughter—and feel better immediately—pop in *Dumb and Dumber*, sign up for a daily joke online, make more lunch dates with that spitfire girlfriend, and share embarrassing moments with coworkers. Look for humor in your everyday routine. And when there *isn't* anything to laugh about, fake it. "Your body doesn't know the difference," says Buxman.

Here's another drill to help you sense your inner energy and find your true voice.

Think of where the back of your throat and nose meet as the top of a funnel emptying to a long tube. Where the tube ends (at your "core," or lower abdomen), there is a rotating propeller ready to spin. As you inhale, imagine the air as water pouring down to start the rotor turning. Let the rotor gain momentum for a few seconds, heat up, then set off an energy that radiates and provides enough power to propel an exhalation in the form of steam. Use this energized stream of air to trigger and manipulate your voice.

The Antistress Diet

When Rebecca Berg, a lawyer with the district attorney's office in Brooklyn, is stressed, dinner is likely to be Peppermint Pattie appetizers followed by a Snickers bar entrée.

Sound familiar?

Most of us don't eat right when we're stressed. Rationally, we know we should, but then the pressure hits and we're grabbing food on the run, skipping meals, and overdosing on premium ice cream and jumbo bags of potato chips.

Yet eating right during stressful times is particularly important because stress affects *how* we use what we eat. When you're stressed, your body absorbs fewer nutrients even as it excretes more, thus increasing your need for the vitamins and minerals found in nutrient-rich foods.

Eating the right foods helps us cope with these changes and ensures that we have the ammunition we need to fight the energy-draining effects of stress. Not only can a well-balanced diet help during times of stress, but how well we eat *before* a stressful event also plays a role in how we handle that event.

The Commandments of Stress-Busting Eating

When you're stressed, you may feel like you only have time to guzzle down a cup of coffee in the morning, while chocolate smothered in chocolate sounds like an appealing lunch. To avoid putting any more stress on you with complicated lists of nutritional guidelines, we've developed the following seven commandments:

Thou Shalt Forgo Coffee. Caffeine only aggravates stress. Just a cup or two of coffee, or any other caffeinated beverage, such as tea or cola, can escalate feelings of anxiety because caffeine directly affects the brain and central nervous system, producing changes in heart rate, respiration, and muscle coordination. That's why we get that jittery feeling when we drink too much caffeine. Coffee can also decrease absorption of certain minerals, like iron, and stress-fighting magnesium.

Thou Shalt Not Skip Meals. When you miss meals, you deprive yourself of the essential building blocks you need to function at your best.

Too little of just one nutrient amplifies the stress you feel by straining the processes in your body that depend on that nutrient. For example, if you deprive your body even slightly of iron, you may become irritable and tired because an iron deficiency decreases the amount of oxygen going to your tissues and brain.

Thou Shalt Eat Breakfast. It's arguably the most important meal. You've just woken up from a long period of fasting, starving your brain of the glucose it needs to function. Ergo, breakfast. It doesn't have to be complicated. A simple bowl of whole-grain cereal topped with fresh fruit and skim milk is an energizing way to start the day.

Thou Shalt Strive for Balance. Research shows that when we eat meals with a high carbohydrate-to-protein ratio (lots of carbohydrates with a little protein), we increase the amount of tryptophan available to our brain. Tryptophan is an amino acid required to manufacture serotonin, a brain chemical that has a calming influence, a plus when we're under stress. High-carbohydrate meals also help keep levels of the stress hormone cortisol under control, while high-protein diets may increase cortisol levels, aggravating feelings of stress. Over the long term, elevated cortisol levels can reduce the brain's ability to use glucose, eventually affecting brain function. High cortisol levels can also lead to overeating, because the hormone affects appetite control chemicals such as serotonin and dopamine.

WOMEN ASK WHY

Why do we tend to turn to sugar when we're stressed?

Although no one knows for sure why sugar has such an allure when we're under pressure, one thing we do know is that humans have an innate liking for sweet foods.

Back when we had to forage for our food, our preference for sweets may have helped keep us alive, because naturally sweet foods like fruits tended to be safe to eat, and bitter foods were often poisonous.

Nowadays, one of the most likely reasons we turn to sugary foods is that we've been programmed to consider these foods as treats. From the time we were children, we were taught to see sweet foods as a reward. As adults, we still look to foods like ice cream, chocolate, and cookies as a reward.

It turns out the ability of these foods to comfort us is not just in our minds. Our sugar cravings may also be biochemical. We are hardwired to love and want sugar (in the form of glucose) because our brains need it to function properly. Sugar also acts as an instant energy booster, interacting with the brain to produce adrenaline. So when we're feeling drained by stress, sugar can act as a quick pick-me-up.

The trouble is that the energy we get from sugar is short-lived, which is why the jump start is often followed by a crash. If you happen to be a sugar craver, it's important to recognize that about yourself so you can better manage your urges.

Expert consulted
Elizabeth Wilen-Berg, Ph.D.
Psychologist/consultant specializing in eating
*   disorders and weight-management issues*
New York City

Thou Shalt Choose the Right Carbohydrate. To get the right building blocks you need to function at peak levels, the focus should be on complex carbohydrates such as whole grains,

THE DE-STRESSING POWER OF TEA

With a bowl of tea, peace can truly spread.
—Sen Shoshitsu, Urasenke Grand Tea Master XV

Ever notice that tea drinkers seem calmer than coffee drinkers? It might be more than just the beverage choice.

Many serious practitioners of tea find that the rituals involved enable them to develop a discipline of mind and body that helps them concentrate on the present moment and put away worries about the past and anxieties about the future. In the frenzied world in which we live, taking time to slowly prepare and drink a hot cup of tea can provide a moment of peace to rest our bodies, empty our minds, and soothe our souls.

In many cultures, tea service and drinking of tea is designed as a soothing ceremony. For example, the Japanese practice an elaborate tea ceremony that transforms the simple details of tea preparation into a thing of beauty and tranquility. The student of tea learns how to arrange the teapot, bowls, and other tools of tea, including how to time each gesture, movement and interlude. Tea time in Japan is not just about drinking tea, it is a time to ponder the four principles of tea—harmony, respect, purity, and tranquility—and to acquire peace of mind.

Similar relaxing tea ceremonies are popular in many other parts of the world, such as China, Russia, India, and England. Here in the United States, while we don't have a tea ceremony of our own, we can learn something from these other cultures.

Next time you feel overwhelmed by the pressures of life, escape to the kitchen to brew a soothing pot of chamomile tea or a decaffeinated black tea. Serve with milk and honey. Savor the time it takes to prepare, and when you sip your tea, see if you can't find a bit of warming calm in your cup.

dangerous territory because vitamin and mineral intake decrease, increasing your susceptibility to the negative effects of stress. Plus, diets high in sugar may increase the loss of calming minerals such as magnesium and chromium.

Thou Shalt Not Ignore Fats. All fat is not "bad" fat. In fact, our bodies actually require some fat in order to survive. But the type of fat you eat is important, especially when you're stressed. Saturated fats (found in red meat, full-fat dairy, and other animal products) and trans fatty acids (found in processed and fast foods, usually in the form of partially hydrogenated oils) can suppress your immune system and raise levels of stress hormones like cortisol. So when you're stressed, focus on healthy fats, such as the monounsaturated fats found in olive and canola oil and the omega-3 fatty acids found in cold-water fish such as salmon and mackerel. These fats won't aggravate the stress response, and the omega-3s may even boost your immunity, a plus during tense times. Still, that's not a license to overindulge. Fat should make up only 30 percent or less of your total calories.

Thou Shalt Get the Right Vitamins and Minerals. The top three stress fighters are vitamin C, the B-complex vitamins, and magnesium. Vitamin C, by boosting your immune system, helps you fight back when stress hits. The best sources of vitamin C are dark green vegetables (like spinach and broccoli), strawber-

fruits, and vegetables. Sugary simple carbohydrates, such as candy and sodas, provide little in the way of nutrients and are really just wasted calories. Also, as sugar intake rises, you enter ries, and citrus fruits. The B-complex vitamins provide added energy to help fight battle fatigue. B-complex vitamins include thiamin, riboflavin, niacin, pantothenic acid, and vitamins B_6 and B_{12}, and are found in a wide variety of foods, including poultry, whole grains, and some vegetables. We tend to lose magnesium when we're stressed, and foods high in magnesium, like nuts, beans, and whole grains, can help replace lost supplies.

Putting It All Together

Here's how the basic principles of antistress eating—three meals a day plus snacks, concentrating on high carbohydrate, moderate protein, and low-fat meals—translates into a week's worth of eating. This meal plan packs a powerful punch of just the right ratio of carbohydrates and protein and emphasizes foods that are high in stress-fighting vitamins and minerals like vitamins B and C and magnesium. For an added nutrient boost, we've included many foods rich in omega-3 fatty acids.

MONDAY

Breakfast
1 cup low-fat or nonfat granola topped with 3/4 cup mixed berries (blueberries, strawberries, and raspberries)

3/4 cup low-fat or nonfat plain yogurt

1 ounce chopped walnuts

Snack
6 ounces vegetable or carrot juice

Lunch
1 serving Tranquil Tuna Slaw with Creamy Lemon-Dill Dressing (page 145)

1 piece whole wheat bread drizzled with 1 teaspoon olive oil

Snack
1 apple

1 ounce reduced-fat cheese

2 rye crispbread crackers

Dinner
2 cups whole wheat pasta with 2 tablespoons Placid Pesto (page 146)

2 cups mixed salad greens with 1 tablespoon nonfat dressing

Snack
2 fig bars

8 ounces fat-free milk (or 1% milk or calcium-fortified soy milk)

Nutrition totals: 1,767 calories, 83 g protein, 284 g carbohydrates, 42 g fat, 52 mg cholesterol, 35 g dietary fiber, 2,098 mg sodium

TUESDAY

Breakfast
1 small low-fat bran muffin

1 egg or 2 egg whites, scrambled

8 ounces fat-free milk (or 1% milk or calcium-fortified soy milk)

Snack
10 baby carrots (buy these ready to eat, or peel and slice regular carrots) dipped in yogurt dressing (mix 1 tablespoon nonfat yogurt with 1 teaspoon fresh chopped parsley, 1 teaspoon lime juice, and a dash of cayenne pepper, if desired)

Lunch
Tomato and mozzarella sandwich (layer about 2 ounces low-fat mozzarella, 1/2 ripe tomato, and a few fresh basil leaves on a slice of seven-grain bread. Drizzle lightly with 1 teaspoon olive oil and 1 teaspoon balsamic vinegar and top with another slice of bread)

1 cup low-sodium vegetable or minestrone soup

Snack

1 cup sliced fruit (try a tropical fruit like papaya or pineapple)

Orange juice spritzer (mix ½ cup orange juice with ½ cup plain seltzer water and add ice)

Dinner

2 cups Soothing Soybean Stew (page 147) served over 1 cup whole wheat couscous

1 cup steamed greens tossed with 1 teaspoon olive oil and 1 teaspoon fresh lemon juice

Snack

1 poached pear (in a small saucepan, bring to a boil ¾ cup water, 2 teaspoons maple syrup, and 1 teaspoon vanilla extract. Boil for 5 minutes, or until syrupy. Reduce the heat and add 1 small peeled pear. Cover and cook, turning the pear and basting occasionally, for about 20 minutes, or until tender but not overdone. Cool in the refrigerator.) with ½ cup nonfat vanilla frozen yogurt

1 tablespoon raisins

Nutrition totals: 1,803 calories, 87 g protein, 256 g carbohydrate, 56 g fat, 250 mg cholesterol, 30 g dietary fiber, 3,156 mg sodium

WEDNESDAY

Breakfast

1½ cups oatmeal topped with 1 tablespoon raisins and 2 teaspoons flaxseeds

1 pink grapefruit

8 ounces fat-free milk (or 1% milk or calcium-fortified soy milk)

Snack

1½ cups Truly Tropical Smoothie (page 148)

Lunch

Jazzy Turkey Sandwich (layer 3 ounces turkey breast, 1 slice reduced-fat cheddar cheese, and ¼ to ½ sliced Granny Smith apple on a slice of whole wheat bread. Top with another slice of bread spread with a mixture of 1 tablespoon prepared horseradish sauce and 2 teaspoons low-fat mayonnaise.)

¾ to ½ Granny Smith apple (remaining from sandwich recipe)

6 ounces cranberry-apple juice

Snack

1 cup lightly steamed vegetables (try zucchini or yellow squash; steam them anytime it's convenient, store in resealable plastic bags, and use within 3 days) dipped in low-fat dressing

Dinner

4 ounces grilled or baked salmon fillet

1 cup cooked brown rice (or other whole grain, such as quinoa or bulgur)

1½ cups Swiss chard (or other dark green, leafy vegetable) sautéed with 2 teaspoons olive oil

Snack

1 large peach (or a serving of another orange-colored fruit, such as ½ mango or 2 apricots)

Nutrition totals: 1,834 calories, 101 g protein, 288 g carbohydrate, 40 g fat, 139 mg cholesterol, 36 g dietary fiber, 1,949 mg sodium

THURSDAY

Breakfast

1 cup bran cereal topped with 1 sliced medium banana and 8 ounces fat-free milk (or 1% milk or calcium-fortified soy milk)

Snack

¾ cup low-fat cottage cheese with ½ cup pineapple chunks (canned in natural juice), sprinkled with 2 teaspoons flaxseeds

Lunch

1 serving Calming Quiche (page 145)

1 small garden salad (2 cups lettuce, 3 or 4 tomato wedges, and 4 or 5 slices cucumber) with nonfat dressing

Snack

2 tablespoons nut butter (try cashew or almond butter as a peanut butter alternative) spread on 2 whole grain crackers

Dinner

2 cups Tranquil Vegetarian Chili (page 145)

1 cup cooked brown rice

Snack

2 graham crackers

8 ounces fat-free milk (or 1% milk or calcium-fortified soy milk). Try warming the milk and serving it with a dash of cinnamon and 1 teaspoon honey.

Nutritional totals: 1,757 calories, 108 g protein, 287 g carbohydrate, 36 g fat, 190 mg cholesterol, 44 g dietary fiber, 4,198 mg sodium (This total is high due to Tranquil Vegetarian Chili, but since it's high for only one day, it averages out fine over the week.)

FRIDAY

Breakfast

2 small whole grain toaster waffles with ½ cup Relaxing Raspberry-Melon Melange (page 146)

8 ounces fat-free milk (or 1% low-fat milk or calcium-fortified soy milk)

Snack

10 to 15 low-fat tortilla chips, dipped in 1 tablespoon salsa

Lunch

Meditative Middle Eastern Pita Pocket (stuff one whole wheat pita with 3 to 4 tablespoons hummus, ¼ cup chopped tomato, ¼ cup chopped cucumber, and ¼ cup chopped romaine lettuce. Add a dash or two of hot sauce if desired.)

1½ cups lentil soup with carrot

Snack

1 small orange cut into sections and dipped in low-fat chocolate syrup

Dinner

4 ounces baked trout (marinate in 2 teaspoons olive oil and the juice of ½ lemon)

1 cup kale (steam, then sauté quickly in 1 teaspoon olive oil with ½ teaspoon chopped garlic)

1 baked sweet potato

1 whole wheat dinner roll

Snack

1 bunch purple grapes (1 to 2 cups)

Nutrition totals: 1,735 calories, 83 g protein, 296 g carbohydrate, 41 g fat, 135 mg cholesterol, 51 g dietary fiber, 2,060 mg sodium

SATURDAY

Breakfast

1 whole wheat bagel topped with 1 tablespoon reduced-fat cream cheese

2 slices fresh tomato

8 ounces fresh grapefruit juice

Snack

8 ounces fat-free milk (or 1% milk or calcium-fortified soy milk)

2 tablespoons walnuts and 2 tablespoons raisins mixed together

Lunch

Simple Chef's Salad (tear 2 cups romaine lettuce into bite-size pieces and top with 1 cup cherry tomatoes, 2 ounces sliced skinless turkey breast, and 1 ounce grated reduced-fat Cheddar cheese)

1 tablespoon low-fat or nonfat creamy dressing

1 piece whole grain toast

Snack
1 slice cantaloupe (about ⅛ medium)

⅓ cup low-fat vanilla yogurt

Dinner
1½ servings Bucolic Beef and Broccoli Stir-Fry (page 148)

Snack
1 cup fruit sorbet

Nutrition totals: 1,787 calories, 105 g protein, 271 g carbohydrate, 40 g fat, 140 mg cholesterol, 23 g dietary fiber, 1,996 mg sodium

SUNDAY

Breakfast
3 (4-inch) whole wheat banana pancakes (add ripe banana slices to whole wheat pancake mix) with ½ cup nonfat vanilla yogurt

6 to 8 ounces orange juice

Snack
2 cups air-popped popcorn

Lunch
1 to 1½ cups low-sodium black bean soup

1 serving Serenity Pizzas with Sun-Dried Tomatoes (page 147)

Snack
8 ounces fat-free milk (or 1% milk or calcium-fortified soy milk)

2 tablespoons almond butter on whole-grain bread

Dinner
4 grilled jumbo shrimp (or 6 large shrimp)

1 serving Relaxing Brown Rice with Spinach and Feta Cheese (page 146)

Snack
1 serving Becalmed Berry Vanilla Pudding Parfaits (below)

Nutrition totals: 1,809 calories, 93 g protein, 263 g carbohydrate, 53 g fat, 371 mg cholesterol (this total is high due to Relaxing Brown Rice with Spinach and Feta Cheese, but it averages out fine over the week), 38 g dietary fiber, 2,677 mg sodium

Becalmed Berry Vanilla Pudding Parfaits

2 large ripe bananas, sliced
1 pt strawberries
16 oz fat-free plain yogurt
About 3 Tbsp superfine sugar

In a food processor, combine the bananas and strawberries and process until smooth. Add the yogurt and sugar and process just until blended. (If your fruit is very sweet, cut back on the sugar. Taste the mixture before freezing to determine how much is needed.) Pour into an 8" × 8" metal baking pan. Freeze for 3 to 4 hours, or just until firm.

Break the frozen yogurt into chunks and return the mixture to the food processor. Process until smooth. Transfer to a freezer container and freeze until solid. Let stand at room temperature for 10 to 15 minutes to soften slightly before scooping.

Makes 5 cups
Per ½ cup: 63 calories, 3 g protein, 13 g carbohydrates, 0.5 g fat, 1 mg cholesterol, 1 g dietary fiber, 35 mg sodium

Tranquil Tuna Slaw with Creamy Lemon-Dill Dressing

¼ c reduced-fat mayonnaise

1 Tbsp lemon juice

1 tsp dried dillweed

1 tsp Dijon mustard

2 c packaged coleslaw mix (see note)

2 cans (6½ oz each) water-packed albacore tuna, drained and flaked

In a medium bowl, mix the mayonnaise, lemon juice, dillweed, and mustard. Add the coleslaw mix and toss to coat. Gently stir in the tuna.

Makes 4 servings

Per serving: 135 calories, 19 g protein, 7 g carbohydrates, 3 g fat, 30 mg cholesterol, 1 g dietary fiber, 449 mg sodium

Note: Buy a coleslaw mix that contains carrots and other vegetables, or add a shredded carrot.

Tranquil Vegetarian Chili

1 large onion, finely chopped

1 green bell pepper, finely chopped

1 small carrot, finely chopped

2 cloves garlic, finely chopped

1 Tbsp olive oil or canola oil

2 tsp chili powder

1 tsp ground cumin

1 can (15 oz) red kidney beans, rinsed and drained

1 can (15 oz) cannellini beans, rinsed and drained

1 can (14½ oz) diced tomatoes (in juice)

1 can (8 oz) tomato sauce

¼ tsp salt

¾ c low fat plain yogurt or reduced-fat sour cream

2 Tbsp chopped fresh cilantro

In a large saucepan over medium heat, cook the onion, pepper, carrot, and garlic in the oil for 10 minutes, or until the vegetables are softened. Stir in the chili powder and cumin. Cook for 2 minutes, stirring often.

Add the kidney beans, cannellini beans, tomatoes (with juice), tomato sauce, and salt. Simmer for 45 minutes over medium-low heat, stirring often. If the mixture becomes too thick, add water as necessary.

Serve topped with a dollop of yogurt or sour cream and sprinkled with cilantro.

Makes 6 cups

Per cup: 196 calories, 10 g protein, 33 g carbohydrates, 3.5 g fat, 2 mg cholesterol, 5 g dietary fiber, 1,167 mg sodium

Calming Quiche

Crust

2½ c cold cooked brown rice

⅓ c grated Parmesan cheese

2 egg whites, lightly beaten, or ¼ c liquid egg substitute

Filling

12 oz low-fat silken tofu

4 eggs, lightly beaten, or 1 c liquid egg substitute

1 Tbsp cornstarch

½ tsp salt

⅛ tsp ground nutmeg

1 lb asparagus, trimmed, cut into 1" pieces, and steamed

3 oz reduced-fat Swiss cheese, shredded

2 oz ham-flavored soy deli slices, finely chopped

2 scallions, finely chopped

Preheat the oven to 350°F. Lightly coat a 10" deep-dish pie plate with cooking spray.

To make the crust: In a large bowl, mix the rice, cheese, and egg whites or egg substitute. Press evenly in the bottom and up the sides of the prepared pie plate. Bake for 15 minutes.

To make the filling: In a food processor, combine the tofu, eggs or egg substitute, cornstarch, salt, and nutmeg. Process until smooth, scraping down the sides of the container as necessary.

Sprinkle the asparagus, cheese, soy slices, and scallions over the baked crust. Pour in the tofu mixture, stirring gently to blend slightly.

Bake for 45 minutes, or until firm in the center. Let stand 5 minutes before slicing.

Makes 6 servings

Per serving: 261 calories, 27 g protein, 25 g carbohydrates, 8.5 g fat, 151 mg cholesterol, 2 g dietary fiber, 524 mg sodium

---

Relaxing Raspberry-Melon Melange

- ¼ c honey or sugar
- 2 Tbsp orange juice
- 2 Tbsp finely chopped crystallized ginger
- ¼ tsp ground ginger
- 1 cantaloupe, cut into ½" cubes
- 1 c raspberries
- ¼ c toasted sliced almonds

In a large bowl, combine the honey or sugar, orange juice, crystallized ginger, and ground ginger. Add the cantaloupe and toss to coat. Refrigerate for at least 2 hours, stirring occasionally. Just before serving, gently stir in the raspberries and almonds.

Makes 3 cups

Per ½ cup: 120 calories, 2 g protein, 23 g carbohydrates, 3.5 g fat, 0 mg cholesterol, 2 g dietary fiber, 10 mg sodium

Placid Pesto

- ⅓ c chopped walnuts
- 2 c packed fresh basil leaves
- ½ c grated Parmesan cheese
- ⅓ c extra-virgin olive oil
- 1–2 cloves garlic, halved
- ⅛ tsp ground black pepper

In a small skillet, stir the walnuts over low heat for 2 minutes, or until golden and fragrant. Let cool, then transfer to a blender or small food processor. Add the basil, cheese, oil, garlic, and pepper. Process until smooth, scraping down the sides of the container as necessary.

Makes 1 cup (enough for 1 pound of pasta)

Per Tbsp: 73 calories, 2 g protein, 1 g carbohydrates, 7 g fat, 2 mg cholesterol, 0 g dietary fiber, 59 mg sodium

Note: Store the pesto in a covered container for up to 5 days in the refrigerator or up to 1 month in the freezer.

Relaxing Brown Rice with Spinach and Feta Cheese

- 1 tsp olive oil
- 1 large onion, finely chopped
- 1 c brown rice
- 2½ c water
- 1 box (10 oz) frozen chopped spinach, thawed and squeezed dry
- 4 oz reduced-fat feta cheese, finely crumbled
- 8 kalamata olives, pitted and finely chopped
- 4 eggs, lightly beaten, or 1 c liquid egg substitute

In a large saucepan, warm the oil over medium heat. Add the onion and cook, stirring frequently, for 5 minutes. Stir in the rice and water. Bring to a boil, then cover, reduce the heat, and simmer for 45 minutes, or until the water has been absorbed. Remove from the heat.

Preheat the oven to 350°F. Coat an 8" × 8" glass baking dish with cooking spray.

Stir the spinach, feta, and olives into the rice. Stir in the eggs or egg substitute. Spoon into the prepared baking dish.

Bake for 25 to 30 minutes, or until a knife inserted in the center comes out clean. Let stand for 5 minutes before serving.

Makes 4 servings

Per serving: 391 calories, 19 g protein, 49 g carbohydrates, 13.5 g fat, 213 mg cholesterol, 5 g dietary fiber, 677 mg sodium

Variation: To turn this into a hearty side dish, omit the eggs.

Serenity Pizzas with Sun-Dried Tomatoes

    4 whole wheat pitas
    1 c water
    1 oz dry-packed sun-dried tomato halves, chopped
    ¼ c tomato paste with Italian seasonings
    1 box (10 oz) chopped frozen spinach, thawed and squeezed dry
    ½ c reduced-fat ricotta cheese
    2 oz shredded provolone cheese
    2 oz shredded reduced-fat mozzarella cheese

Preheat oven to 400°F. Arrange the pitas on a baking sheet.

In a small saucepan, stir together the water, tomatoes, and tomato paste. Bring to a boil over medium heat. Reduce the heat to low and simmer for 5 minutes. Spread evenly over the pitas.

In a small bowl, combine the spinach and ri-

cotta. Spoon evenly over the pitas. Sprinkle with the provolone and mozzarella.

Bake for 10 to 12 minutes, or until the cheese is melted and the pitas are slightly crisp. Let stand 5 minutes before serving.

Makes 4

Per pizza: 279 calories, 18 g protein, 34 g carbohydrates, 8.5 g fat, 28 mg cholesterol, 3 g dietary fiber, 680 mg sodium

Soothing Soybean Stew

    1   Tbsp olive oil
    1   large onion, finely chopped
    ½   c finely chopped green bell pepper
    1   Tbsp finely chopped garlic
    1½   tsp ground cumin
    1½   tsp ground coriander
    ¾   tsp ground ginger
    1   small butternut squash, peeled, seeded, and cut into ½" cubes
    2   c water
    2   cans (15 oz each) soybeans, rinsed and drained
    1   can (8 oz) tomato sauce
    1½   tsp salt

In a large saucepan, warm the oil over medium heat. Add the onion and cook, stirring constantly, for 3 minutes. Add the pepper, garlic, cumin, coriander, and ginger. Cook, stirring constantly, for 2 minutes. Stir in the squash and 1 cup of the water. Bring to a boil. Reduce heat to medium-low, cover, and simmer for 5 minutes.

Stir in the soybeans, tomato sauce, salt, and the remaining cup of water. Simmer for 20 minutes, or until thick.

Makes 6 cups

Per cup: 192 calories, 12 g protein, 21 g carbohydrates, 8.2 g fat, 0 mg cholesterol, 4 g dietary fiber, 543 mg sodium

Bucolic Beef and Broccoli Stir-Fry

  1 c cooked brown rice
  1 Tbsp canola oil
  ¾ lb top round, thinly sliced
  1 bunch scallions, cut into 1" pieces
  2 c broccoli florets
  ½ c water
  3 Tbsp reduced-sodium soy sauce
 1½ tsp sesame oil

In a large nonstick skillet, warm the canola oil over medium-high heat. Add the beef and cook, stirring constantly, for 1 minute, or until browned on all sides. Remove from the pan and set aside.

Add the scallions to the pan. Cook, stirring, for 1 minute. Add the broccoli and cook, stirring, for 1 minute. Add the water, soy sauce, and sesame oil. Cook, stirring often, for 5 minutes, or until the vegetables are tender. Stir in the beef and heat through. Serve over the rice.

Makes 4 servings
Per serving: 385 calories, 26 g protein, 47 g carbohydrates, 10.5 g fat, 40 mg cholesterol, 3 g dietary fiber, 464 mg sodium

Truly Tropical Smoothie

  1 c low-fat plain yogurt
  1 c mango cubes
  1 small banana, sliced
  ½ c pineapple chunks
  ¼ c nonfat dry milk
  1 Tbsp lime juice

In a blender, combine the yogurt, mango, banana, pineapple, dry milk, and lime juice. Blend until smooth.

Makes 3 cups
Per 1½ cups: 230 calories, 10 g protein, 45 g carbohydrates, 2.5 g fat, 9 mg cholesterol, 3 g dietary fiber, 129 mg sodium

Note: For a thicker, icy-cold drink, freeze the fruit first (keep a supply of fruit chunks in the freezer for instant smoothies).

Calming Herbs and Supplements

Ever hear this one? Question: "How many women with PMS does it take to change a lightbulb?" Answer: "What—is that supposed to be some kind of joke?!" You could just as easily remove the reference to PMS and add the word *stressed* in front of *women*, and the joke would still ring true.

What few of us realize, however, is that we needn't stand still and allow ourselves to be eroded by stress. A potpourri of herbal supplements can build up body and mind, rendering us more resistant to the effects of stress. Some work as antidotes to general stress, while others deal with specific stress symptoms, such as headaches and anxiety.

The Many Shades of Stress

Think of your body as having within it a life force, vitality, or simply the will to live, says Douglas Schar, a member of the National Institute of Medical Herbalists in the United Kingdom and an herbalist in Washington, D.C. Then consider that vitality—energy, chi, or vibrancy—as a flame. When it burns brightly, in-

fections can't get in—they bounce off your body. When the flame diminishes, however, disease creeps in. When the flame goes out, we die. Stress is responsible for much of the loss of that vitality, draining our life force, Schar says. And with diminished vitality, we're prone to all kinds of physical illnesses.

The purpose of the herbs outlined here is to help maintain that flame of life. But they are as individual as the woman who takes them. So if you're looking to bust some stress, find an herb that addresses your particular needs, Schar suggests. The better the match, the better the effect.

It's also important to realize that simply sipping a cup of life-force-boosting herbal tea or taking a few drops of vitality-invigorating tincture won't magically whisk away all stress, Schar says. You need to work on your whole being to achieve wellness—including incorporating exercise and a healthy diet.

Composite Stress

This is the stress that comes from simply being alive. Unfortunately, we can't control some of these varied stresses because they're life's drama. There's psychological stress, such as death, marriage, and emotional overdrive; environmental stress, such as chemical and bacterial pollution, food additives, even the weather; and physical stress, such as too much typing at work or sitting in traffic.

Herbs for combating composite stress are called *adaptogens* because they help us *adapt* better to our environment.

Siberian ginseng. People who go "off coffee" sometimes try Siberian ginseng (*Eleutherococcus senticosus*) to add a little pep to their mornings. But it can also add a little pep to life.

As one of the first herbs to be termed adaptogenic, Siberian ginseng was used by the Russian cosmonauts to help them adapt to the lunar environment. It can also be used during stressful times (such as the week before your daughter's wedding) to maintain your energy and prevent a post-event illness, and during airline flights across many time zones to stave off fatigue and immune decline.

Dosage: Take it three times a day during periods of stress for as long as you need it. Try four 500-milligram dried bark tablets or capsules. Or take 1 teaspoon of 1:5 tincture. Make sure you're using *Siberian* ginseng, notes Schar, and not its Asian or American cousins, which can wreak havoc on your menstrual cycle or worsen menopause symptoms.

Astragalus. *Astragalus membranaceus* has been used for hundreds of years for its ability to strengthen resistance to disease. Modern herbalists recognize it as an endurance booster.

Dosage: Because it takes several weeks to establish itself in the body, you need to take astra-

MAGNESIUM: NATURE'S TRANQUILIZER?

Even though we have only about an ounce of this mineral in our bodies, magnesium is present in nearly all of our cells to help us produce energy. It aids in building proteins, maintaining our teeth and muscles, and regulating our immune and nervous systems. It also seems to protect against heart disease.

But it may also help calm us down.

In two studies in the United Kingdom, women with PMS were given magnesium to see if their "symptoms" would decrease.

In the first study, the women experienced significantly less fluid retention after 2 months of daily, 200-milligram doses of magnesium, as well as less anxiety, depression, and cravings, says Ann F. Walker, Ph.D., senior lecturer in human nutrition at the University of Reading in England.

In Dr. Walker's second study, 44 women were given either 200 milligrams of magnesium, 50 milligrams of vitamin B_6, a combination of the two, or a placebo every day during their menstrual cycles. Those who received the magnesium plus the B_6 significantly reduced their anxiety-related PMS symptoms, including nervous tension, mood swings, and irritability.

The reason?

galus for at least 3 months and up to 2 years to benefit from its adaptogenic properties. Take two 500-milligram dried root tablets or capsules or 1 teaspoon of 1:5 tincture. Be sure you're using a product that contains astragalus *root* and only the root, says Schar.

Oat straw. *Avena sativa* has been around for a dozen centuries as a folk remedy for nervous exhaustion and depression. It also helps with endurance, burnout, recovery from surgery or illness, and even withdrawal from addictive substances.

Dosage. You'll need to take it for at least a month before you notice its effects, but it's

"It's likely that even a marginal magnesium deficit upsets the balance of the neurotransmitters serotonin and dopamine in the brain," says Dr. Walker. "Magnesium supplementation may help to restore this balance—but it's all still speculation."

Although Dr. Walker sees no reason why we couldn't start supplementing magnesium to ease anxiety, she says a change in diet is a better option.

"There's a lot of marginal magnesium deficiency in modern life due to the low intake of whole grains, nuts, seeds, and beans. High intakes of calcium may also reduce magnesium absorption even if you're eating a whole grain, healthy diet," she says. The best dietary sources of magnesium are nuts such as cashews, legumes (such as navy beans, pinto beans, and black-eyed peas), whole grains, green veggies (such as spinach, broccoli, and green beans), artichokes, and tofu.

If you supplement, try 150 milligrams of magnesium citrate or chelate, recommends Dr. Walker. You may not feel the full effects for a couple months and if you're taking calcium supplements, your calcium-to-magnesium ratio should be 2:1, she says. Supplemental magnesium may cause diarrhea in some people, and if you have heart or kidney problems, check with your doctor before you begin supplementing in any amount.

okay for long-term use, Schar says. Take 1 teaspoon of 1:5 tincture three times a day. Be sure to buy a pure product without any other herbs added, says Schar. While it's safe for working women juggling career and family, it shouldn't be used if you're allergic to gluten (celiac disease).

System Stress

Think of this stress as specific to the various systems in the body. Some of us get headaches, some get stomachaches, and others may experience menstrual irregularities.

That's because stress has a habit of landing on our weakest link, says Schar. In addition to the general anti-stress herbs, herbal medicine offers systemic tonics that strengthen whichever system is being ravaged by stress.

"They are boosters for your weak link," says Schar.

Nervous Stress

This stress involves the things that, frankly, stress us out—divorce, having three kids, paying the bills. It affects the emotions and the nervous system, which functions with the help of neurotransmitters in the brain. All this thinking begins to wear out the nervous system, which then needs a nerve tonic to boost neurotransmitter levels. The helpful herbs include:

St. John's wort. Several studies have documented the positive effects *Hypericum perforatum* has on mild depression. But it's also effective for burnout, when your nervous system has simply had enough. Not only does it help you cope better with the things you can't control, such as the morning commute, but it may also help repair damaged nerves, says Schar.

Dosage. St. John's wort can be taken long term—for years, if necessary. It must be taken consistently for at least a month or two before you feel its effects. Take one dose three times a day. One dose is equivalent to two 500-milligram dried herb tablets or capsules or 1 teaspoon of 1:5 tincture. Since it can cause phototsensitivity, avoid too much direct sunlight while taking it. Also, don't take it with antidepressants or other prescription drugs without discussing it with your doctor.

Immune Stress

Modern life gives the immune system a lot of work. Instead of dealing with a manageable number of bacteria, viruses, and fungi, we have to fight off a higher, almost unnatural number. Your office is a prime example, says Schar. The circulated air systems in many offices today spew the bacteria of all your coworkers on you throughout the day. The same goes for air travel, where you share the air—and any infections—with your fellow passengers. The immune system is also stressed when we're not eating right, sleeping well, or exercising—adding up to a potentially lethal combination. Problems, says Schar, include constant infections, rheumatoid arthritis, allergies, and eczema. Immune stress calls for an immune tonic to help out this beleaguered system.

Echinacea. At the first signs of a cold, many people opt for a few doses of the purple coneflower (*Echinacea angustifolia* or *E. purpurea*). This immune enhancer was used by early American settlers (thanks to advice from the Native Americans) to heal snakebites and infected wounds. It stimulates the body's own infection, bacteria, and virus fighters, helping prevent secondary infections, such as pneumonia, bronchitis, and tonsillitis. It can also help your body get rid of other infections, such as urinary tract infections, for good. Taken during times of stress, when your immune system is weak, it can help you avoid the often inevitable cold, Schar says.

Dosage. While echinacea can be used long-term, stop taking it once you feel better for several days. Take three doses a day. Use 1 teaspoon dried root in 1 cup boiled water, two 500-milligram root tablets or capsules, or 1 teaspoon of 1:5 tincture. If you're allergic to plants such as ragweed, asters, or chrysanthemums, don't use products made with echinacea flowers. Don't use echinacea if you have tuberculosis, lupus, multiple sclerosis, or leukemia.

HOMEOPATHIC TREATMENTS FOR STRESS AND ANXIETY

Homeopathy is a natural pharmaceutical science that uses very small and specially prepared doses of substances to stimulate and strengthen your overall immune and defense system, says Dana Ullman, director of Homeopathic Educational Services in Berkeley, California, and author of *Homeopathy A–Z*.

The basis of homeopathy is the identification of a substance in nature that would, if given in large doses, *cause* the very symptoms the ill person has. Because symptoms are the body's way of fighting infection and/or adapting to stress, finding such a substance and using it in minute doses augments the body's own ability to heal itself, Ullman says.

A homeopathic practitioner treats stress symptoms by examining the characteristic way you respond to stress and then finding a substance in nature that mimics and/or causes similar symptoms to the ones you're experiencing, Ullman says. Those symptoms, he says, represent your body's best efforts to deal with the stress.

There are hundreds of possible homeopathic remedies for stress, each of which is chosen based on the unique physical and psychological responses each person would have to it, says Ullman. Some of the most common remedies he recommends include the following.

Kali phosphoricum (potassium phosphate). Try this if you're stressed from anxiety, overwork, or too much excitement, which usually exhibits itself in significant fatigue and/or depression. Take 6x or 6c potencies three times a day as needed for no more than 3 days. If there isn't significant improvement by then, says Ullman, it probably isn't the correct remedy.

Ignatia (St. Ignatius bean). This remedy can aid conditions brought on by acute emotional stress, such as grief, fear, anger, embarrassment, or a scolding. During an emotional crisis, take a single dose of the 30x or 30c potency. If symptoms don't improve in 6 to 8 hours, repeat the dose. If they're still not better, find another remedy. If symptoms do improve, repeat dose only when they worsen. Don't take more than twice a day for 3 days.

Natrum muriaticum (table salt). This remedy is appropriate if you become ill after an emotional trauma, such as a loss or rejection or a reprimand or if you have easily hurt feelings. Take a 6x or 6c potency three times a day, as needed. It's rarely necessary to take it for more than 3 days, says Ullman.

You may also decide to see a practitioner trained in homeopathy if you feel chronically stressed or if the above remedies don't work for you, suggests Ullman.

"They'll look for a 'constitutional remedy,'" Ullman says, which is prescribed based upon your genetic endowment, your personal health history, and your overall physical and psychological characteristics. "It's a powerful way of strengthening the person."

To find a homeopathic practitioner near you, check out the Homeopathic Educational Services Web site at www.homeopathic.com. They will provide a listing with any purchase.

You can also visit the National Center for Homeopathy's Web site at www.homeopathic.org. Costs for consultations vary widely, since many homeopaths are also medical doctors, Ullman says.

Reproductive Stress

This is the stress that results in problems with your menstrual cycle, or the stress that infertility treatments or hormone replacement therapy places on your body.

To ease reproductive stress, try the following herb.

Vitex. *Vitex agnus-castus* balances hormone levels, whether they're too high or too low. It works on the pituitary gland in the brain to curb production of the hormone prolactin. Less prolactin helps normalize an irregular menstrual cycle. Also known as chasteberry, vitex is also used to help with very heavy bleeding, spotting, severe hot flashes, extreme PMS, low libido, and the dizziness that occurs as we near menopause. It's also helpful for time-of-the-month acne flare-ups and digestive upsets.

Dosage. Vitex must be used for at least 3 months before you see improvement, and it can be taken indefinitely. (Once your hormone levels normalize, however, this new balance may become permanent, so you might not need to continue taking it.) Take one dose every morning at the same time. You can take $1/2$ teaspoon of the seeds boiled in a cup of water, two 500-milligram tablets or capsules, or 50 drops of a 1:5 tincture. Buy products made of vitex *berries* without any other herbs. If you experience spotting between periods, see your health care provider, says Schar.

Respiratory Stress

We're talking classic colds, flu, and coughs here. Try the following:

Licorice. If 5,000 years of use in China is any indication, a dose of licorice root (*Glycyrrhiza glabra*) can aid virtually any problem of the chest. Similar to our own natural steroids, licorice helps improve inflammatory conditions such as asthma, says Schar. It also contains antiallergic and antibronchitic actions—a bonus for

VITAMIN C: A STRESS BUSTER?

Because psychological stress affects the immune system, you run an increased risk of infectious diseases, such as cold viruses. Vitamin C can help bolster your immune system to prevent stress-related health problems.

The vitamin appears to work by suppressing the adrenal glands' response to stress by inhibiting their secretion of the stress hormone glucocorticoid.

Increasing your intake of vitamin C when you're stressed helps reduce the incidence of illness and disease often associated with stress, says Sam Campbell, Ph.D., chair of the department of biological sciences at the University of Alabama in Huntsville. He led a study that supported a vitamin C–glucocorticoid stress-reduction connection.

In that study, lab rats were stressed and then given either 200 milligrams of vitamin C or nothing. Those receiving the vitamin had lower levels of the stress hormone glucocorticoid—as well as fewer other physical signals of stress.

To boost your levels of vitamin C, eat red chile peppers, red and green bell peppers, kale, parsley, broccoli, brussels sprouts, cabbage, strawberries, cantaloupe, and citrus fruits. Or take 100 milligrams at breakfast and another 100 milligrams with dinner to keep up blood levels of vitamin C throughout the day—up to 1,000 milligrams a day is within safe limits.

asthmatics and the elderly, who are more vulnerable to coughs and colds.

Dosage. Licorice can raise blood pressure if it's taken long-term, so stop taking it for at least 2 weeks after 6 weeks of use. Take three doses every day and you should feel the effects quickly, says Schar. A dose is 1 teaspoon of dried root boiled in 1 cup water and strained, two 500-milligram dried root tablets or capsules, or 1 teaspoon of 1:5 tincture. Don't take licorice if you have diabetes, high blood pressure, liver or

kidney disorders, low potassium levels, or water retention.

Urinary Tract Stress

The last thing you need when you're buzzing around checking things off your to-do lists is a bathroom break every 5 minutes. But that's the sort of interference a urinary tract infection (UTI) causes. Here's an herb that may help you combat UTIs.

Uva-ursi. A cousin of the cranberry, *Arctostaphylos uva-ursi* was recognized by the medical community as a treatment for UTIs until the advent of antibiotics. In addition to fighting infection, uva-ursi reduces the pain associated with UTIs and cystitis. And, unlike antibiotics, uva-ursi can end the vicious cycle of repeated UTIs, says Schar.

Dosage. To clear an infection, use it for 2 weeks, three times a day, says Schar. One dose is the equivalent of 1 teaspoon of the dried herb boiled in water, two 500-milligram dried herb tablets or capsules, or 1 teaspoon of 1:5 tincture. Do not use for more than 2 weeks without the supervision of a qualified practitioner. Don't use during pregnancy or if you have kidney disease or damage. Uva-ursi may cause stomach upset. If you develop a high temperature or back pain, see your doctor immediately.

Cardiovascular Stress

Schar attributes this country's increase in heart disease during the past century, in part, to the increase in work-related stress. One herb stands out as a heart helper.

Hawthorn. Shown to lower blood pressure, LDL ("bad") cholesterol, and platelet stickiness, *Crataegus oxycantha* (and *C. laevigata* and *C. monogyna*) has also been shown to increase circulation to the heart as well as improve the health of the blood vessels that service the heart muscle, says Schar. Hawthorn is widely prescribed in modern-day Europe for many heart-related maladies.

Dosage. To help prevent or improve heart disease, hawthorn can be taken three times a day for the rest of your life, says Schar. One dose is 1 teaspoon of 1:5 tincture. Because it lowers blood pressure, be sure to discuss any hawthorn use with your doctor, and don't stop taking your heart medicines without consulting her. If you have a cardiovascular condition, do not take hawthorn regularly for more than a few weeks without medical supervision. You may require lower doses of some other medications, such as high blood pressure drugs. If you have low blood pressure caused by heart valve problems, do not use hawthorn without medical supervision.

Moving into Calm

Those small, everyday stresses that we all experience—that flat tire, being late for work, the argument with your boss—add up. Studies show that the cumulative effects of these daily annoyances are much more likely to contribute to the development (or worsening) of physical and psychological health problems, including anxiety and depression, than "major life events" such as divorce or the death of a spouse. Indeed, daily minor stress has been linked to increased blood pressure and muscle tension and a lowered immune response.

One of the best ways to combat all that?

Get moving.

In a study conducted at the University of Texas M. D. Anderson Cancer Center in Houston, researchers found that recreational activities such as running, basketball, and aerobics classes reduced the physical symptoms and anxiety associated with minor stresses. What's more, the research indicated, not surprisingly, that the more we exercise, the more benefits we're likely to get.

According to the researchers, participating in leisure activities may help minimize stress-related symptoms by providing a "time-out period" that distracts us from our stress in the first place. It also gives us a sense of accomplishment that instills self-confidence and lifts our spirits.

There are other theories about how exercise helps people manage stress. One is that the well-recognized cardiovascular benefits of some forms of exercise, such as jogging or running, help you cope better with stress. Another is that endorphins and other brain chemicals that are released during exercise make you feel better—some even call it a "high"—not only while you're exercising but after the fact as well.

But for exercise to work its magic, it has to be something you look forward to, not just another task on your already too long to-do list.

Though many experts cite the value of 30 minutes of moderate aerobic exercise, the American College of Sports Medicine says you can divide your exercise into two or three 10-minute sessions throughout the day to reduce stress, as well as strengthen the heart and other muscles. Aerobic activities such as walking, running, swimming, and biking are great. Yard work, housework, or dancing to a peppy CD are other activities that will do the trick just as well.

As little as 10 minutes of moderate exercise—a brisk walk or some yoga stretches—can leave you feeling more relaxed and energetic for up to 2 hours.

If you combine that exercise with meditative techniques, such as those taught in yoga or tai chi, so much the better. These mind-motion activities not only promote balance and flexibility but bring about mental calm as well.

Oodles of Exercises: How to Choose

While different forms of exercise have different benefits, there is no *best* exercise for stress relief. It all depends on your individual skills, motivation, experience, and interests.

Sharon Brown, Ph.D., assistant professor of physical education and exercise science at Transylvania University in Lexington, Kentucky, for example, says she isn't particularly flexible, so yoga would frustrate her and be stressful. A 4-mile run, however, is something that she *does* do well, and it never fails to lift her spirits.

"Even better," she says, "is running with friends. This encourages me to exercise; plus, my friends help me find healthy perspectives and solutions to situations at work and with relationships."

On the other side of the exercise equation is Peggy Elam, Ph.D., a New York City psychologist and yoga buff. She frequently recommends this ancient discipline to her clients as a way to deal with their own stress.

FOCUSING WITH FELDENKRAIS

Like yoga and other forms of movement-meditation, Feldenkrais (pronounced FELD-en-krise), teaches you to focus and to be aware of your movements. Especially good if you suffer from chronic pain, Feldenkrais—which was invented by Russian physicist Moshe Feldenkrais in the 1940s—is composed of two types of lessons.

In the *awareness-through-movement* lessons, a teacher leads a group class in more than 1,000 different movement lessons, focusing on such everyday activities as sitting, standing, reaching, and bending down. The teacher uses a combination of imagery, visualization, and hands-on manipulation to help students focus on how they move.

Functional integration lessons are usually given on a one-to-one basis and involve more hands-on attention on the part of the teacher. A Feldenkrais practitioner guides her student through different movements, helping the student learn more efficient ways to move.

To find a Feldenkrais teacher or practitioner, contact the Feldenkrais Guild of North America at (800) 775-2118, or visit the Web site www.feldenkrais.com. Members are certified and have graduated from accredited training programs. The guild also has continuing education requirements for its certified practitioners.

The key is discovering what works best for you and finding the right balance. If the exercise is too easy, you'll get bored. Too strenuous, and you'll feel even more anxious, especially if you're not used to exercising in the first place. In fact, while you may think that strenuous exercise is the best way to vent your frustrations, researchers at the University of Georgia in Athens found that anxiety levels decreased most during the *lowest*-intensity exercises, such as walking.

Most important, however, is doing something you like. If you're just starting out and aren't in very good shape, walking might be your best bet. If you're already fit and want to step up the pace a bit, you might consider a faster-paced aerobic workout such as kickboxing.

And for safe, gentle exercise that blends meditation and relaxation techniques, yoga and tai chi might be the answer. Almost anyone, any age, any fitness level, can do them. (If you have a chronic condition, such as heart disease or back pain, or if you are pregnant, consult your physician first. Once you get the go-ahead, let the instructor know your situation that so she can work with you.)

Now that you know *why* you should exercise, it's time to decide *how*. Don't know where to start? Here are brief descriptions of some of the best ways to move "into the calm."

The Activity of Aerobics

The word *aerobic* was first used in the late 1960s by Kenneth Cooper, M.D., who designed aerobics programs for astronauts and pilots and is largely credited with starting the fitness craze in the 1970s. "Aerobics" translates literally into *with oxygen*. When you exercise, your body needs additional oxygen, which is then delivered to your muscles. Ergo, aerobics.

If you participate in aerobic exercise on a regular basis, studies show, you'll have more energy and feel less anxiety, tension, apprehension, depression, and fatigue, compared to nonexercisers. You'll also improve your self-esteem and respond better to life's little obstacles than someone who doesn't exercise regularly. Aerobic exercise comes in many forms—walking, jogging, running, biking, swimming, and dancing, to name a few. What they all have in common, though, is the ability to work your heart and your lungs. To accomplish this, you generally have to use your large muscles, such as your arms, legs, back, chest, and buttocks.

The various forms of aerobic exercise create a *training effect*, which strengthens the heart and

working muscles, increases the respiratory system's capacity to take in air and exchange oxygen for carbon dioxide, and strengthens the immune and hormonal systems. During physical activity itself, all of these systems are "jogged" (no pun intended) into action. Even about 90 minutes after a good workout, you'll still have a feeling of deep relaxation.

The least expensive forms of aerobic exercise are jogging, running, and walking. All you need are a good pair of shoes and the right clothes and you can exercise all year round. But before you start a jogging or running program, schedule a physical examination with your doctor—especially if you're over 50. An exercise stress test, usually on a treadmill, should be part of the examination. This test detects cardiovascular problems that you might not be aware of.

Start with the right equipment. That's rubber-soled tennis or running shoes that support your foot, fit comfortably, and help absorb the shock of the foot when it hits the ground. The right socks (thick or thin) may also help prevent blisters.

Dress right. When you're just starting out, you can wear almost anything that's comfortable. But as your fitness level increases, so will your desire for better gear. For warm-weather walking, jogging, or running, wear shorts and a cotton shirt. When it gets colder, put on clothes that will pull moisture away from your skin. CoolMax or other synthetic fibers designed for activewear will work, because they wick away sweat. You can dress in layers, but don't wear cotton next to your skin, because the moisture builds up. Polar fleece headbands and gloves are a good idea for antimoisture gear, as well.

Measure your progress. When you start exercising, run or walk as far as you can in 12 minutes. After a month, do it again and note your improvement. Start slowly. You should be able to talk and jog at the same time. If you're panting or breathing hard, stop jogging and walk for a while.

Swimming is another excellent aerobic exercise with the bonus that it puts less stress on your joints. The downside, of course, is that you need access to a pool year-round. Most communities have YMCAs or community centers, with both indoor and outdoor pools, and many local universities allow the public to use their pools. Sometimes hotels allow the public to use their pools for a small fee.

Biking is also a great aerobic exercise, good not only for cardiovascular conditioning but also for weight control, stress relief, and as a form of energy-saving transportation. It does require that you own a bike and know how to ride skillfully, especially in traffic. On the plus side, it's an activity that can be done alone or with others, and it's a great way to get some fresh air and enjoy a change of scenery.

Dancing is another form of aerobic exercise that can help you control your weight, reduce your stress, and tone up your heart and lungs. There are many types of dancing—including disco, rock and roll, folk, aerobic, ballet, tap, jazz, and modern. The social activity of dancing in groups can also lift your spirits, but if time is short, go ahead and put a tape or CD in the stereo and dance around your living room.

The Yin and Yang of Yoga

The word *yoga* means "union" in Sanskrit, the ancient language of India. Yoga was developed as a Hindu tradition of spiritual, physical, and mental discipline, comprising different approaches to self-realization or enlightenment. Although yoga originated within Hinduism, it is not a religion in itself. In fact, the meditative aspects of yoga can help people of any religion feel a greater connection with their own spirituality.

Yoga was first introduced to the Western world by Swami Vivekananda in 1883 and first became popular in the United States during the 1960s, when the "flower children" generation began to explore Eastern practices and philosophies. Since then, American yoga teachers such as Richard Hittleman and Lillias Folan have exposed yoga to a wider audience through their books, television programs, and videotapes. Even more people became interested in this ancient practice in the 1990s as celebrities such as Madonna, Sting, Ali MacGraw, and Jane Fonda took it up. Many doctors, including such well-known physicians as Dean Ornish, M.D., and Andrew Weil, M.D., have jumped on the yoga bandwagon as well, recommending it as a preventive health measure as well as for stress relief.

Hatha yoga is the most commonly practiced form of yoga in the United States. The word *hatha* means forceful, and the syllables of *ha* and *tha* have also been interpreted as symbolizing the union of the energies of the sun and the moon.

Paul Smith, a yoga instructor at the Lake Austin Spa Resort in Texas, describes hatha yoga as a physically active form of exercise that seeks to bring together the physical body with the mental and spiritual bodies. The benefits include better body awareness and posture, strengthening of the back (which may help to prevent or control chronic lower-back pain), and development of overall strength and flexibility.

The meditative aspects of yoga classes can increase mental clarity and focus, he says. Yoga is also thought to improve different systems of the body by clearing blockages and opening channels of energy and vitality.

Many yoga students find that the practice of yoga also offers them metaphors for their own life. Peggy Elam, the psychologist who not only recommends yoga to her clients but practices it herself, noticed that as soon as she starts to compare her own position to that of other people in class, she loses her balance. It doesn't matter whether she's coming out ahead or behind in the comparison, just that as soon as her focus shifts, she starts to wobble. "That's an effective lesson for our lives in general," she says.

A typical yoga class begins with breath-control exercises (*pranayama*) designed to clear the mind and open the lungs, followed by the series of yoga postures or poses known as *asanas*. The objective of the *asanas* is to move the spine through its complete range of motion and to promote flexibility and strength throughout the entire musculoskeletal system.

Asanas fall into five categories: standing, seated, prone, supine, and inverted (or upside-down). The poses can be held for a few seconds or—more strenuously—a few minutes. If the pose involves stretching, as many yoga postures do, remember to stretch slowly and gently and to stop if you feel any pain.

Some traditional yoga positions are thought to increase the risk of neck and knee injuries. If you have knee or back problems, an experienced, certified or registered yoga teacher can help you modify *asanas* to stay within a range of motion that is safe for you. If you have glaucoma or high blood pressure, be careful about breath retentions and inverted poses.

All forms of hatha yoga have similar goals of conditioning the body and fostering the interaction among the body, mind, and spirit, says Smith. There are, however, subtle differences among the different styles of yoga. A class described simply as hatha yoga may be a combination of these approaches.

DE-STRESSING YOGA POSES

When you don't have time for a complete yoga workout, run through a few postures to ease stress and fatigue. Yoga teacher Cyndi Lee, director of the OM Yoga Center in New York, suggests these poses.

Lion (Simhasana). Sit with your legs tucked under your buttocks, toes pointing back, and hands on your knees,

palms down. Taking a deep breath in through your nose, lift your buttocks slightly off your heels, curl your torso forward, make two fists, squeeze your face, and tense your entire body. As you exhale, drop back onto your heels, open your chest, reach forward with your arms at shoulder level, and spread your fingers wide. Open your eyes, and, looking up to the middle of your forehead, open your mouth wide and stick your tongue out toward your chin.

This pose seems funny at first, but it is effective for increasing circulation in the throat, an area that holds a lot of tension. Lee says the lion pose helps prevent sore throats, purifies bad breath, and improves clarity of speech. Because it brings focus and energy to the head, the lion pose is also said to relieve emotional distress. So before doing this posture, take a moment to think about what mental baggage you want to discharge. Then, when you exhale, let it go. Repeat this pose three to five times.

Legs Up the Wall (Viparita Karani). This pose is excellent for easing fatigue and decreasing swelling in the feet and legs. According to yoga teachings, by reversing the usual flow of energy in the lower body, blood and lymph fluid pool into the abdomen, nourishing the pelvic belly and removing tension from overworked legs. This pose can be more restful than a short nap because it restores the circulatory system while we are still and quiet, calm yet awake.

Find a quiet corner or an empty wall and lie down on your

back, with your legs up the wall. Experiment with the distance between your buttocks and the wall until you're comfortable. Try to keep your legs straight and relaxed as they lean against the wall. Keep your heels together. Feel your chest and belly dropping into ur back, and feel your back dropping into the floor. Let your arms fall open to your sides, palms up. For a more open position of the chest, place your arms overhead, elbows relaxed. Close your eyes and pay attention to your breath flowing in and out naturally. You can stay in this position for up to 20 minutes.

Shoulder and Chest Opener. This pose opens the chest, rib cage, throat, and heart chakra and creates flexibility in the muscles of the respiratory system, allowing you to breathe more deeply and fully. When your chest and lungs are sunken, your breathing becomes shallow, exacerbating tension.

Sit cross-legged on the floor with a cushion under your buttocks, or sit on the front edge of a chair or stool with your feet flat on the floor. Interlace your fingers behind your back and press your palms together (if you can). Reach toward the floor with your thumbs and index fingers as you lift your chest and face toward the ceiling. Try to keep a sense of length in the back of the neck as you lift your face. Inhale and exhale deeply. Visualize your breath opening the spaces between each rib, be-

tween your shoulder blades, and between your ears. Stay like this for five deep breaths. Inhale. Sit up. Exhale and rest.

❧ Anusara yoga is an integrated approach in which the human spirit blends with the science of biomechanics. Anusara yoga emphasizes attitude, alignment, and action.

❧ Ashtanga yoga (sometimes called Power Yoga), is a vigorous style that the singer and actress Madonna has popularized. It consists of a set sequence of poses that build strength and flexibility.

❧ The yoga of Bikram Choudhury, director of the Yoga College of India, consists of an exact set of 26 postures performed in a warm, humid room (at least 80 degrees). As with ashtanga, it's a vigorous, strength-building style.

❧ Iyengar yoga is a detail-oriented practice, building strength and alignment through postures that emphasize technique. Iyengar yoga makes frequent use of props such as blocks, belts, blankets, and chairs to assist in the poses.

❧ Jivamukti yoga has the pace of ashtanga yoga but incorporates spiritual teachings.

❧ Kripalu yoga emphasizes *pranayama* (breath work).

❧ Kundalini yoga involves breathing, chanting, and meditation to achieve therapeutic rejuvenation—realigning the body systems and the chakras (the body's energy centers).

❧ Sivananda and Integral styles integrate yoga practice into a holistic lifestyle, including positive thinking and vegetarianism. The goal of these styles is for the body to be easeful, the mind peaceful, and the life useful.

❧ Viniyoga encourages the practitioner to feel comfortable and steady,

WOMAN TO WOMAN

Yoga Changed Her Life

Kris Kuss is no stranger to exercise. For years, the 33-year-old information architect for a new media agency has been a competitive cyclist and a runner. About 4 years ago, Kris's boyfriend suggested that she add yoga to her already busy schedule. That decision, she says, has changed her life. This is her story.

We're all so emotionally—and physically—stressed. There's never enough time, and there are always so many people and things depending upon us. What yoga has taught me is a new way of thinking.

Instead of being involved "in the moment," yoga persuades you to approach situations from a "witness" standpoint. It takes you out of the situation so that you're not so emotionally invested. You learn not to blindly react. This is, of course, nothing we haven't all heard before, but now it all makes sense to me.

The practice of yoga has also taught me how to physically relax. When I'm stressed, I tend to be really tense. I don't even notice it until I come back to myself and pay attention to how taut I am. Now I can teach myself to relax.

I look forward to the end of every yoga practice, when everyone lies in the *corpse* position for what is called "final relaxation." For 10 minutes, lying flat on my back, completely at rest, I'm able to "flush out" stress, leaving myself with the sense that I've gone to a different land and come back.

Yoga also gives me more flexibility, balance, and a better sense of my own body. Plus, I have less inner turmoil, and it shows. A friend of mine said to me, "You seem wonderfully enraptured these days, almost in love with where your life is at the moment. . . . The biggest change I see in you is that you accept most things as they are, and when you see a pained thing as immovable, you move on."

While I wouldn't describe myself quite so glowingly, I think my friend has the idea. Inherent in yogic philosophy is "be here now." I have a greater appreciation of what I have, and I take a lot less for granted.

adjusting the poses to one's needs.

Each style of yoga has a slightly different emphasis, with the teacher integrating the traditions and presenting them through her understanding and personality. Before taking a yoga class, talk to the teacher about her philosophy, teaching style, and experience, and find out whether she is a registered yoga teacher. If you have medical limitations, ask if the instructor understands your condition or has worked with other students who have it. Then try a class you think will best meet your goals. Afterward, ask the instructor for feedback.

You can find classes posted on bulletin boards in health food stores or libraries, in the yellow pages, or by word of mouth.

Until recently, there were no uniform standards of certification for yoga teachers, but an organization called the Yoga Alliance has begun registering teachers with 200 to 500 hours of training. To find a registered teacher, visit the organization's Web site at www.yogaalliance.org. For other questions, contact the Yoga Alliance Registry of Yoga Teachers at 877-YOGA-ALL (964-2255), e-mail the organization at info@yogaalliance.org, or write to 120 South 3rd Avenue, West Reading, PA 19611.

Between yoga classes, you should practice at home. All you need are a small, uncluttered space and a small rug or exercise mat. To get the consistent benefits of yoga, try to practice regularly. You don't need to do your entire routine of *asanas*, just three or four different ones that include forward, lateral, and backward bending; spinal twisting; and at least 5 minutes of meditation each time. Twenty to 30 minutes, every day or every other day, suffices for a good home workout.

Tai Chi: The Moving Meditation

Stroll through a public park in China on any given day and you're likely to see groups of elderly people performing a series of gently flowing, graceful movements. They're doing *tai chi chuan*, or *tai chi* for short, an ancient discipline that's been called "moving meditation." This martial art stresses overall wellness. The benefits of tai chi include a calm mind, increased coordination and balance, improved flexibility, and stress reduction.

In one Atlanta study, 15 weeks of tai chi training helped 200 elderly people cut their risk of falling almost in half and significantly reduced their blood pressure.

In China, tai chi is the basis of traditional Chinese medicine, explains practitioner Jim Hill of Lutherville, Maryland, and its changing series of postures are designed to bring about a harmonious flow of energy (known in Chinese medicine as *qi* and pronounced "chee"). The movements are performed slowly so that you can focus on movement, breathing, quieting the mind, and relaxing the body.

The "ultimate low-impact exercise," tai chi can be done safely by almost anyone who can stand or walk.

To find a tai chi class, check out community centers, senior centers, health clubs, and martial arts academies. There is no centralized certification organization, so ask the prospective instructor about his training and background. Tai

DE-STRESSING PLACES
An Ashram

Feel like you just want to run away? Well, sometimes that is the best prescription (don't forget to leave a note, though!). But where to go? How about an ashram?

Ashrams have existed in Eastern countries since the earliest civilizations as centers of meditation, spiritual practice, and learning. But you don't need to travel halfway around the world to find an ashram. Today these spiritual centers are scattered throughout the United States, dedicated to promoting the harmony of spiritual, mental, and physical values. You can visit www.ashram.com to locate one near you, or anywhere else in the world.

Located in the foothills of the Catskill Mountains, a little more than an hour from New York City, for example, is Ananda Ashram, the country retreat of the Yoga Society of New York. At Ananda, you can participate in the ashram lifestyle for a day, a weekend . . . or for much longer.

A typical weekend program at Ananda Ashram begins with dinner Friday evening, followed by meditation and an introduction to the program. Saturday and Sunday are filled with yoga, meditation, guest lectures or classes, and cultural programs.

Ananda is open year-round and provides a restful retreat for those interested in meditation, the teachings of yoga and vedanta (a philosophy that declares the "oneness of all beings in the Supreme Spirit"), and East-West cultural exchange. It is located at 13 Sapphire Road, Monroe, NY 10950, or look for information on its Web site, www.anandaashram.org.

chi is handed down from teacher to student, says Hill, and a tai chi instructor must have been given permission by her teacher to pass on the lessons.

It's difficult to learn the movements through books or videotapes, but once you learn them with the help of a tai chi guide, you'll be able to do them on your own.

Not for the Beginner: Kickboxing

Kickboxing is an ancient martial art that has been popularized in recent years under the name of Tae-Bo. While Tae-Bo may indeed lower your stress, a word of advice . . . it's not for beginners.

Tae-Bo, created by martial arts champion Billy Blank, features a nonstop routine of high steps, kicks, and punches set to lively music. It combines the intensity of a high-impact aerobic class with the self-defense moves of the martial art of kickboxing. As a result, Tae-Bo can burn a lot of calories—up to 450 per hour for a 135-pound woman, according to a study conducted at the University of Mississippi.

Many experts think cardio-kickboxing moves are risky and increase your chances of hip, knee, and low-back injuries. If you're interested in pursuing kickboxing, then, look for an instructor who has been certified by the American Council on Exercise (ACE) or the national YMCA.

If you're not already in tip-top shape before signing up for kickboxing, spend a few weeks improving your overall fitness level with some aerobic exercise.

The Ultimate Escape

In 1997, Sherrine Hakim was an insurance adjuster working 80-hour weeks and living out of hotel rooms. Today she's crewing a sailboat with her new boyfriend, traveling around the world to interview people from other cultures for a series of television shows.

Kirsten van Aalst was living in a 450-square-foot apartment in New York City, commuting 3 hours a day to her job in Connecticut, often with less than $5 in her pocket. Today she's raising her daughter in Vermont in a log cabin on 12.5 acres with a view of a mountain and a 40-minute commute to her job at a local university.

And Emily MacLean struggled with bank loans and car payments, coordinating catering events and bartending 60 hours a week while trying to squeeze in a writing career. Today she's producing a movie from her own script, which she wrote while on a 6-month sabbatical in Paris.

Nice fairy tales, you think, but here in the real world, I have a deadline in 20 minutes, my kids are sick, my car's in the shop, and my husband's this close to getting laid off. Me, live on a mountain in Vermont? Fat chance!

Here's the kicker: You can. Hundreds of thousands of women have already reengineered their entire lives. They're part of a trend of formerly stressed, unfulfilled people making radical changes to realign their lives with their values. What do these renegades have that we don't? Well, it's not empty schedules or bottomless bank accounts, or even childless freedom. What they have is something everyone has access to: clarity. They've figured out what it is they *really* want to do and are going for it with everything they're worth.

The American Dream Deferred

Most of us follow the road maps given to us by our parents, our bosses, our peers: get a degree, build a career, buy the largest house you can afford. Dress for success. Spend money to make money. Greed is good.

But where has this left us? According to the Center for a New American Dream, a nonprofit organization providing information and resources to people who want to simplify their lifestyles, 1998 saw more than 1.4 million families declaring personal bankruptcy. Credit card debt has climbed to an all-time high. Personal

BLAME IT ON STRESS

Overspending

In the same way that others use alcohol or drugs to destress, some women spend money as a coping mechanism, according to Esther Maddux, Ph.D., professor emeritus in financial management at the University of Georgia in Athens.

Spending is either planned, impulsive, or compulsive. Planned spending is thought out and controlled, like buying a car after researching the safest and best models. Impulsive spending is acting without deliberation, such as getting 40 rolls of toilet paper because you hit a great sale. Compulsive spending, however, is when you have a nearly physical need to spend money. You may feel upset or sad, but instead of going to the gym or to a friend's house, your first impulse is to head to the mall and burn up the credit card. Compulsive spenders use buying to cope with stress, escape demands, or overcome uncomfortable situations, Dr. Maddux says.

Compared with other women, compulsive buyers tend to have lower self-esteem. They may also be more materialistic, envious, and prone to fantasy. They don't necessarily want to own the items they buy; they derive all their psychological benefits from the buying process itself. Indeed, they use "things" as a way to boost their feelings about themselves.

If you normally control your spending but see it rise during times of stress, it's probably impulsive. You're probably buying for convenience, and as long as you can afford it, it shouldn't be a major problem. But if you feel an almost physical need to buy something, and you don't *really* believe you'll ever have to pay for it—despite the credit card bills—that's compulsive.

As you move toward higher self-esteem, you will naturally cut back and not have the need to spend. As with recovering from other addictions, moving from life-diminishing to life-enhancing behavior will help remind you how hard you worked for that money, and you won't have the compulsion to buy.

savings is at its lowest rate since the Depression. The average American worker logs 47 hours per week. We're tired, stressed, overextended—all in the name of success.

But what happens when we question that reality? When, instead, we embrace the alternative: *Less is more.*

Total changers trade stress for less—less worry, less work, less people pleasing, less empty spending. And sometimes, yes, less money. What they tend to gain seems eminently more satisfying: Serenity. Fulfillment. Passion. And time.

Who Are These People?

Contrary to the experience of Diane Keaton's character in the movie *Baby Boom*, not all total changers move from the city to the country and have baby, boyfriend, and business neatly sewn up in the span of 2 hours. Total change takes many forms.

Sometimes it means changing financial habits or exchanging parenting roles with your mate or starting your own business. The key is that total changers live the lives they choose, not the lives that chose them.

"These women live *deliberately*," says Janet Luhrs, author of *The Simple Living Guide* and editor for almost 10 years of *The Simple Living Journal*. "They know what their focus is, they stop trying to please everyone, and suddenly everything just becomes a lot clearer."

Esther Maddux, Ph.D., professor emeritus in financial management at the University of Georgia in Athens, spent years getting advanced degrees and climbing the university ladder. Then she had a revelation—she wanted to help people in a different way. So she became a financial advisor, leaving her high-profile academic career behind. She continues to study this phenomenon, which she refers to as the "veil being pulled from our eyes."

"Total changers suddenly have a clearer vision about who they are and what they need," she says. "They become aware of their unfinished business, identify their unmet needs, and are able to satisfy them in meaningful ways."

Why Do They Do It?

Total change is different from the normal job hunt or house upgrade, says Andrea Van Steenhouse, Ph.D., a psychologist in Denver and author of *A Woman's Guide to a Simpler Life.*

"People can agonize over a job change for months, or years," says Dr. Van Steenhouse. "Once you realize you need a total change, it takes on a life of its own."

The wake-up call can come from several situations.

A severe shock. When her best friend died unexpectedly, Shauna Cook, 38, took a hard look at her demanding career as marketing director of an international company based in Madison, Wisconsin. "My friend's death was the slap in the face," says Cook. "I knew I had to do something to give my life more balance."

Cook wanted to explore writing, teaching, spending time with family—things that were being crowded out by her desire to do well at work. So she gave herself a demotion.

A family-time famine. Before her total change, Luhrs had credit card debt, a demanding law career, and a house bursting with stuff. After her first baby was born, it took exactly 2 weeks of leaving the baby home with a nanny for Janet to realize this life wasn't for her. So she left her law career and began working from home, converted her basement into an apartment for rental income, and reverted to a lifestyle of living within her means. This included attacking her credit card debt and reducing her impulse shopping—all of which enabled her to stay home with her child.

A deluge of clutter. Piles of possessions can choke out even your most deeply felt dreams. All that nonessential stuff you buy because it's on sale or you think it will make your life better is really masking an inner need, says William D. Anton, Ph.D., director of the University of South Florida's Counseling Center for Human Development in Tampa.

"When people are focused on external symbols to prove their self-worth, they often work harder to accumulate an endless supply of evidence," Dr. Anton says. Total changers have come to realize this connection and no longer want materialism to rule their lives.

A sense of environmental necessity. A study sponsored by the Merck Family Fund, an endowment that supports environmental programs throughout the United States, found that many Americans think excessive materialism may be impacting the environment.

According to the Center for a New American Dream, Americans already produce twice as much garbage as Europeans. As less prosperous countries develop their economies, they may emulate our current definition of wealth and drive ever-larger, gas-guzzling cars, instead of walking or riding bikes. Eat heavily processed, packaged food instead of cooking from scratch. Buy three TVs instead of spending time with family. The center believes total changers may help save the planet by "shifting American culture away from its current emphasis on consumption and toward a more fulfilling and sustainable way of life." (See www.newdream.org for more information.)

A reemerging creative dream. After a round of cutoffs forced her from a rewarding job and into an administrative role, Marina Stamos, 37, knew she had to make a change. Taking a page out of Luhrs's book, she converted half her house into a rental property, figuring the income would free her up to pursue her creative writing endeavors and to investigate her next career path. One year later, she quit her job, started writing a book, and got a job as a writer and producer for a local television studio.

She credits her success to her resolve. "I knew that if I wasn't happy with the way my life was, I could change," she says.

Total Change Cautions

Don't kid yourself; total change can be risky. "There are no blueprints where you're going," says Dr. Maddux. "It's really hard to figure out who you are for yourself—and it continues to be hard." Instead of relying on your paycheck or your performance evaluation or the brand of jeans you wear, you yourself have to define your self-worth.

To make matters more challenging, your family and friends may try to change you back. When you reject a lifestyle your loved ones consistently follow, your choice can feel like an attack on all they hold dear, says Kathleen Sexton-Radek, Ph.D., professor of psychology

ON THE FRONT LINES
A Female Executive

When Shauna Cook, 38, interviewed for a marketing assistant job at a major power tool company, she could see that the company's plans for growth were ambitious. She pitched herself as the person who could help make it happen.

Boy, did she. The company grew almost 700 percent in 3 years. As director of marketing, with a staff of 10, Cook's stress level grew as dramatically as the company.

Being partially responsible for the marketing strategy of a $200 million power tool company, Cook's life revolved around work. Her 50-plus-hour workweek was meeting-packed, both with upper management (to assure them that the work was getting done) and other departments (to make sure that it did).

Most of Cook's stress came from events beyond her control. For instance, working for a family-owned business, with the family's tight control on decision-making, added another layer of stress that might not have existed at a publicly traded company.

Then there was her role as a manager. For instance, after motivating her team to tackle five of many impossible deadlines during an especially grueling week, her CEO popped into a meeting unexpectedly. "He said, 'Guess what! We have a NASCAR sponsorship! Can we have a car design done by this weekend?'" she recalls. "The air just went out of the room. The team had been totally fired up, and his announcement completely deflated everyone. Then it was my job to build them back up again."

And although Cook was successful at negotiating the

at Elmhurst College in Elmhurst, Illinois. You may even lose the relationship altogether.

That's why it's important to be firm in your knowledge of self before you attempt a total change, says Dr. Van Steenhouse. Otherwise, others' doubts may lead you to question what is how life is," says Dr. Sexton-Radek. "If we decided something and just went off on our way, we would be like robots." Give yourself permission to feel the fear as you push off and follow that dream.

Making the Decision

Here's how some total changers came to their decisions.

Get back to basics: Who am I? There's a reason that "Know thyself" is the fundamental message of thinkers from Plato to Shakespeare. Before you can radically alter your life, you have to know how you feel about your life right now. This may even be the number-one way to minimize stress, says Dr. Van Steenhouse. "Once you've clarified your values, you can get on with what you really want to do—keeping up with the Joneses won't be so compelling," she says.

Embrace responsibility for your true self. The critical part of making a change is truly believing that what you want is what's best. This runs contrary to the instincts of many women's instincts, says Dr. Maddux, especially those who grew up being controlled or manipulated and whose selves have retreated deep within.

" 'Accept responsibility' sounds like something a father shouts at his teenage son, but actually it's incredibly liberating," says Dr. Maddux. "Once we realize we have complete control of our own destiny, we have more of a self to share with our loved ones."

Label your thoughts. Janet Luhrs used the following meditation method successfully during her own total change.

hourly, daily, and weekly deadlines of work, she wasn't able to sort out priorities in another major area—her personal life. Her work schedule rarely afforded her the time to spend with her nephews and her close-knit family. "Sometimes I thought, 'This company could fold tomorrow, and what would I have left?'" she says.

So, in 2000, Cook decided to make a change. Her best friend's death early that year forced her to take a good look at her own life. While she wasn't sure what her life would eventually look like, she knew she wanted more freedom, and she knew it would take some planning.

When preparing her 1999 tax returns with her accountant, she set up her 2000 records so that she'd be ready to make the switch to a home-based business, if that was her decision. She worked with a financial planner to create a viable money plan in case her income was reduced. She read books on consulting and talked to friends who had already made a shift. She closely examined her insurance, budget, and living situation through the eyes of a person with a less reliable income.

After 6 months of contemplation and planning, she made the leap and accepted a new position within her company entailing a 30 percent cut in pay for a 30-hour workweek and a less stressful life.

"I still have an income and the satisfaction of working on projects I love at a company I respect," she explains. "But come 30 hours, I'm done. I have more time to investigate other things I'm interested in, like writing, teaching, consulting, and hanging with my nephews."

Cook opted for a total change and bought herself some peace.

really right for you. "We are often alarmed by others' changes because they highlight our own conflicts," says Dr. Van Steenhouse.

Take heart as you follow your heart. "For every decision, there's no straight line from the idea to the execution—it's jagged because that's

Spend 10 quiet minutes with your eyes closed, by yourself—even if you have to lock yourself in the bathroom. As your thoughts come up, give each a one-word label. For example, if you're concerned about your mom's health, you could call that "worry." If you're mentally listing the food you need at the supermarket, you could call that "planning." As soon as you name the thought, allow your mind to release it. Then allow your attention to flow easily to the next topic.

"It's not about keeping track of all this mental chatter—it's about giving a name to your thoughts," says Luhrs. "As I brought this awareness into the rest of my life, I had a better idea of how I felt about things as they happened during the day."

Journaling is another way to label your thoughts. "Don't give yourself a format—it's not to be graded or poetic; it's simply your thoughts and emotions," says Dr. Van Steenhouse. Also, do not read your writing right away— let it ripen. It's surprising how much more insightful your writing is when it's "brewed" for a while. Journal for 2 to 3 months, but don't share it with anyone. This introspection is a gift to yourself. Honor it and keep it close.

Refine your focus: How do I want to feel? Once you know how you feel right now, you can begin to home in on how you *want* to feel. One way to do that is to begin pushing yourself with some more specific questions, says Dr. Van Steenhouse. Try these.

- When was the last time I felt good?
- Who was I before I got this job (or joined this marriage or had this baby)?

DE-STRESSING PLACES
Omega Institute for Holistic Studies, Rhinebeck, New York

Women's Edge writer Mariska van Aalst decided to check out a de-stressing place in person. Here is her review.

I've had a rough week: three deadlines, my grandmother's passing, an upsetting fight with a friend. Citing my full schedule, I protest as my husband sticks me in the car and says, "Go."

Oblivious, I drive past upstate New York's split-rail fences and horse farms, focused on *getting there*. At the entrance to the Omega Institute, a smiling man in dreadlocks welcomes me and shows me where to park. Another smiling man takes my luggage, which will magically reappear at my cabin doorstep. Everyone is smiling, I realize, and it's impossible not to respond in kind. I feel like I've landed in a warm, outstretched palm.

Omega's original facility rests on 140 acres of pristine woodlands in the Hudson Valley, 2 hours north of New York City. Founded in 1977, this nonprofit center offers 3- to 5-day retreats and workshops with people like Deepak Chopra, Marianne Williamson, and Wayne W. Dyer, each of whom espouses Omega's mission: "To contribute to the world through the transformation of people's consciousness and the healing of their daily lives." Sounds great to me. I can sure use some healing.

After orientation Friday evening, my Yoga and Walking workshop begins. Garrett and Ila Sarley, creators of Natural Yoga ("a system for complete physical, emotional, and spiritual vitality"), lead the 70 participants through some basic poses. Afterward, I stop in at the Wellness Center for a free sauna and a peek at the extras: massage, aromatherapy, astrological readings, acupuncture, and other services starting

- What did I used to dream about?
- What did I want to be when I grew up?
- What did I think I'd know about?

"When people start remembering these

at $35. Back in my cabin, I feel a million miles from home. Crickets lull me to sleep.

Saturday morning at sunrise, I walk to the Sanctuary, where my bare feet are greeted by its soft, well-sanded wood. I sit on a pillow and, with 10 others, face a woman with flowing hair. She taps a wooden stick on her prayer bowl, and the chime signals the start of 20 minutes of meditation. My thoughts ricochet around my head with the force of a pinball machine. As if she can tell, the leader whispers, "Where are your thoughts? Release them and bring your mind back to your breath." We take our time "coming out," letting our eyes fall open slowly and taking full breaths of air.

The rumble in my belly coincides with three tones from a conch shell, calling everyone to breakfast in the high-ceilinged dining hall. Friendships quickly form as we serve ourselves from a selection of scrambled eggs, muffins, organic oat cereal, honeydew melon, miso soup, five fruit juices, and four organic coffees. Other meals feature hummus and bok choy, tofu with spicy black bean sauce, sweet potato burritos and brown rice and beans, all so tasty that I reconsider vegetarianism.

After breakfast, I discover a hammock next to the lake just calling my name. My attention is fully absorbed by the blue sky and the smell of fallen leaves. The weekend unfolds in a stream of yoga, walking, and daydreaming. Hours pass slowly, and by Sunday afternoon, I think, "This has been the longest weekend of my life." For once, that's a very good thing.

The details. A 3-day retreat begins at $110 (including a 1-hour massage) and a 23-day workshop starts at $165. Housing and food start at $145 for a single room with a shared bath and meals. (You can check the institute's Web site at www.eomega.org)

Closing In: What Do I Want to Do?

Now you can start to make some choices. If you're lucky, you've been tinkering with a passion for years and you just need a little nudge to bolster your courage. If you're not sure what it is, try these focusing techniques.

Cut the clutter. Many people begin their journey to a total change by cleaning out their closets. "Clearing away clutter is deceptively powerful," says Dr. Van Steenhouse. "You like the clarity, and you want your inner life to be the way this outer life feels." Giving away old clothes or throwing out unfinished projects—without guilt—frees our energies to look ahead to the next chapter.

Take a solo voyage. Relish a day at the beach, a long drive into the mountains, or an overnight at an inexpensive motel with a large bathtub—alone. Getting away physically removes you from all the static that can be clouding your decision, says Dr. Sexton-Radek. "When you're exploring your options, change—in tempo, in foods, in the way the light shines—helps you think differently and hear your own thoughts and voice more clearly."

Visualize your new life. While you're on your solo voyage, or locked behind the bathroom door, ask yourself some of these questions.

❧ When in my life have I had a feeling that I want to have again?
❧ What are some words that go with that feeling?
❧ What would a picture of this time look like?

things, they often can't believe what they've forgotten," says Dr. Van Steenhouse. Uncovering these hidden passions takes us one step closer to inviting them back into our lives.

RESOURCES FOR A TOTAL CHANGE

- *It's Only Too Late If You Don't Start Now: How to Create Your Second Life at Any Age* by Barbara Sher
- *Live the Life You Love* by Barbara Sher
- *Your Money or Your Life* by Joe Dominguez and Vicki Robin
- *The Simple Living Guide* by Janet Luhrs
- *Six Months Off* by Hope Dlugozima, James Scott, and David Sharp
- *Work as a Spiritual Practice* by Lewis Richmond
- *A Woman's Guide to a Simpler Life* by Andrea Van Steenhouse and Doris A. Fuller
- *What Color Is Your Parachute?* by Richard Nelson Bolles
- *Walden* by Henry David Thoreau
- www.simpleliving.net
- www.newdream.org

- Where would I see myself in the picture?
- Who are the other people in the picture?
- What are the people around me like?
- What's the tenor of the environment?
- What's the physical feel of it—softness, springtime, humidity?

Now take these words and images and . . .

Go to the library. Read books by people who have done what you're considering. Or hit the computer, starting at a search engine like www.google.com. Type in one word from your visualization and wander aimlessly through sites, following hyperlinks wherever they take you. These random associations will spark ideas within you as well as show you thousands of potential resources, says Dr. Van Steenhouse.

Surround yourself with like-minded people. If you're wondering about painting, observe an art class. Considering a job on a sailboat? Sign up to crew for a race. "Whatever moves you—music, science, whatever it is—get yourself into that environment as quickly as possible, in any capacity," says Stamos. "Being there

will show you possibilities you can't imagine while sitting in your living room."

Find a hero. Many total changers attribute their courage to their having a hero, a person whose life they were inspired to emulate. For Dr. Van Steenhouse, it was an Amish farmer whose serenity and order she coveted for herself. For Cook, it was a former bank vice president who eventually became her financial planner. For Stamos, it was her dancer friend. "I would see her perform and think, 'Here's a girl just like me—she's not the fairy godmother with special powers that she portrays on stage. She has problems with her boyfriend; she has a cat,'" recalls Stamos. "Seeing her doing her thing gave me the push I needed to break out."

Avoid the achievement trap. Just because you're interested in writing doesn't mean you have to start winning Pulitzers next week. If you're starting off on a new venture, allow yourself to be a beginner, says Dr. Van Steenhouse. Approach your choice with openness and energy, but most of all with humor. Delight in the process of learning instead of achieving.

Define your bottom lines. It's easy to get carried away when you first think about making a big change. If you're going to move, why stop at the mountains? Why not move to the Himalayas?

Relax. You don't need to change *everything* to make a total change. If you've been practicing your thought labels, you already know what you can let go of and what you can't.

One quick way to incorporate limits in your life is to set stricter hours at work, says Dr. Maddux. "When people have a firmer schedule, they have an increased sense of focus that may help them work faster. If you want to see how much work you can get done in fewer hours, this is a good way to start."

The Money Question

There's a reason that money factors into most total changes—but not because we don't have enough, says Dr. Maddux. Rather than being the shackles that chain us to our current situation, money is a powerful tool that can pave the path to freedom. "Getting control of your finances expands your options dramatically," she says.

Do a financial inventory. As part of their nine-step plan to build financial independence, Vicki Robin and Joe Dominguez, authors of *Your Money or Your Life*, advocate writing down every cent that comes into and goes out of your life. "Part of accepting responsibility for your life is seeing where your money is going," says Dr. Maddux. "If more is going out than coming in, it's time to set goals. Ask yourself what you really want your money to accomplish."

Take it in stages. Moving from New York to Vermont may seem like a sudden change, but van Aalst and her husband planned it for 5 years. Every move was broken into mini-steps: They built the job skills that would allow them to shine in a smaller market. She found a new position, moved in with a friend, then found an apartment. Her husband joined her 1 month later, telecommuted with his old firm until his last project was done, then found a job locally. They paid down their credit card debt, reduced their spending, walked whenever possible, and took their time hunting for a house. When their dream home became available, they were ready.

Live beneath your means. Instead of living on 100 percent of your income, experiment with 90 or 80 percent. When you get a raise or a windfall, sock it away in your total change account. At the reduced percentage, your more frivolous spending will become apparent. "Be-

cause you're confident about who you are, you can find ways to take care of yourself without spending money," says Dr. Maddux. "You can be clear about your priorities so you can spend your money on what you really want."

Think creatively about new cash sources. When Stamos first considered renting out space in her home, she was dubious. "I've given up total privacy, something I might not have believed was an option," she says. "But these short-term sacrifices are helping to make my career switch viable."

Do without. While we all make our own choices about what's important, total changers say they surprised themselves with how little they need. Stamos gave up having her kitchen to herself but now finds she enjoys sharing it with roommates. Janet must choose to be discerning about how she spends her money, but she's watching her children grow up.

"I've made my peace with poverty," says Emily, who's sinking her life savings into her movie. "I know I will never have an expensive car—but when I think of what I'm getting in exchange, I could not possibly care less."

Your Secret Weapon: Commitment

All total changers agree: once you've decided to make the leap, leaning on your resolve can carry you through the roughest of times. "I knew I'd be willing to dig ditches before I would go back to New York," says van Aalst. "Our top priority is staying in Vermont, no matter what it takes."

Whenever Stamos would waver about her decision, she took out this quote from the German poet Goethe: "Until one is committed there is always hesitancy, the chance to draw back, always ineffectiveness. . . . Whatever you can do, or dream you can, begin it. Boldness has genius, power, and magic in it. Begin it now."

Index

Underscored page references indicate boxed text. **Boldfaced** references indicate illustrations.